Ta- La- Vue Publishing
P.O. Box 942
Pottstown, PA 19464

Copyrights: 2008
ISBN: 978- 0-9797521-1-7
Written and story by Charlie Bassett Jr.
Typesetting by George Murrille
Editing by V.R. Editing
Proofreader Tandra T. Rambert
Cover by Tony Lew

Printed in the United States of America

ACKNOWLEDGMENTS

All praise is due to the creator.

Sa`ibah my love, thank you for your tireless support in helping me to achieve my goals.

I also want to thank everyone who rendered support in the production, buying, and selling of this book.

DEDICATION

To My Struggle.

FRIENDS

WRITTEN & STORY

BY

CHARLIE BASSETT JR.

CHAPTER

1

Tracy parked her 2008 Pathfinder at the curb outside of the abortion clinic. She turned her head to the right, fixing her eyes on her friend Dawn who sat nervously in the passenger seat appearing to contemplate an enormous decision. But she really wasn't. Dawn's mind was made up three weeks earlier when her gynecologist confirmed her pregnancy.

As she sat in the car avoiding eye contact with Tracy, Dawn reaffirmed her vision that having a baby at this junction in her life would simply be bad timing.

"You don't have to do this...I can pull off and we can go get something to eat and talk about it," Tracy said.

"There's nothing to discuss, my mind is made up."

"Dawn, this isn't right," Tracy said with emphasis.

"It's not right for you. I have to do what works for Dawn. Thank you for taking off from work to be with me...come on."

Dawn cracked open the car door. She placed one leg outside of the car and paused when she noticed that Tracy wasn't making any attempt to exit the vehicle along with her.

"I can't go inside there."

"What?"

Dawn moved her leg back in the car but left the door ajar.

"You know how I feel about abortions. It goes against my beliefs --"

"You sound like a fucking Republican," Dawn interrupted.

Tracy was offended by the accusation because she was a faithful Democrat and Dawn knew it. In spite of her anger, Tracy held her emotions at bay and just stared straight ahead, watching pedestrians cross the intersection.

Although Dawn glared at Tracy disappointingly, Dawn's feelings were short-lived. She understood the circumstances; this was her situation and hers alone to deal with. She made the call, now it was time for her to walk the walk. But Dawn wasn't going to leave without taking a stab at making Tracy feel guilty.

"You know what Tracy, sometimes friendship needs to be tested," Dawn said snobbishly.

While Tracy was trying to figure out what Dawn had meant by her statement, Dawn inhaled the tense air inside the car and released it out of her nostrils. She opened the car door wider, and without words or second thoughts, she got out of the car. With the heaviest footsteps she had ever taken in her thirty years, she plodded toward the clinic.

When Dawn reached the door of the clinic, she stopped and looked back over her shoulder at Tracy. Both women greeted the other with sad eyes. Dawn was first to turn away before disappearing into the clinic.

While she waited, Tracy clicked on a CD and adjusted the volume to low. She closed her eyes, protruded her full lips, and nodded her head to the music while being disgusted with the decision by her friend of ten years. *If you didn't want to get pregnant you should've used fucking protection*, Tracy wanted to yell out.

As the minutes passed slowly, Tracy grew even more disgusted with Dawn's decision to terminate the pregnancy. Tracy's anger was deeper than religion or politics. It was jealousy. It wasn't the jealousy that contained the ingredients of resentment or malice. It was that unspoken or never-hinted-to envy that one friend may harbor for the other.

Tracy reflected on Dawn's life: Dawn was a lawyer in the prime of her life and childless. Dawn didn't have a care in the world, Tracy assumed. *So why not bring a child in the world you selfish bitch?* Again, Tracy wanted to yell out her thoughts.

As for Tracy's life, things for her weren't peaches and cream. She had moved out of her mother's house when she was seventeen, stumbling from one hardship to the next. She also bounced from one dead-end job to another and rented shabby apartments along the way. As far as men went, if there was a group of fifty eligible bachelors in a room and only one loser among the bunch, rest assured that somehow Tracy would wind up with the loser.

Considering all the trials in Tracy's life, there was one bright spot; her five year old daughter Tammy, who canceled out "all the bullshit," as Tracy would put it. And more recently, as far as men went, Tracy believed her luck with them had taken a turn for the better, thanks to her new boyfriend Rob, the pretty boy who Dawn had hooked her up with three months ago.

Tracy glanced at her watch, then she looked toward the clinic, hoping that Dawn would exit the clinic to reveal that she had changed her mind. But like most things that Tracy wished for, this would be another desire that would not come to pass.

As Tracy sat impatiently in her world of thoughts, a welcoming interruption came with the ringing of her cell phone. She looked at the number and then answered.

"Hello? What's up Sam? I'm outside the clinic waiting for Dawn," Tracy said before frowning as she listened to the caller.

...

Sam sat in her 4x7 cubicle holding the phone wedged to her ear and wagging her index finger in the air as she talked with Tracy on the other end of the phone.

"I heard he's talking about firing you! I told you not to take off -- you only been here two weeks and how many times you taken off already? No, fuck that! Fuck Dawn, she always thinking about her damn self! I'm not trying to hear

3

that shit, she got you down there waiting for her, now you might not have a job. Is she going to get you a job at that law firm she works at?" Sam listened for a moment then further complained, "Tracy, you know I don't even like standing next to that fat motherfucker -- okay -- okay, bye."

Sam hung up the phone and placed her hand over her mouth to muzzle the loud grunt she would have otherwise blared out. She slipped her feet into her three-inch strapped heels that elevated the foul-mouth statuesque to well over six feet. When Sam was frequently asked why she wasn't a model, she would hold up four fingers. When asked about the four fingers, she would respond, "A husband and three kids."

Sam adjusted her skirt and headed across the room toward her supervisor's office. As she walked, she made it a point to sway her ass, knowing that she was being watched by jealous co-workers. Because of Sam's height and beauty, she believed that every woman, including some men, was jealous of her.

When Sam arrived at the supervisor's office, she took a deep breath, rolled her eyes, and then knocked tenderly on the door. Seconds later the door was opened by a short, chubby man wearing an Armani suit and sporting designer glasses. Neither the suit nor the glasses made any improvement to the man's image or unappealing looks.

"Hey, Anthony, can I speak with you a minute?" Sam asked politely as she forced a difficult smile.

"Sure, come in."

Anthony walked over and sat on the edge of the desk as he watched Sam enter while closing the door behind herself. The first thing Sam noticed was the aroma of Anthony's cologne. At that moment, she hated herself for liking the fragrance.

"I want to speak with you about Tracy...she had an emergency today --"

"Why didn't she call in? She hasn't worked here longer than two weeks and has already had two emergencies. What's going on? Does she have a second job as a paramedic?" Anthony said with a snicker as he wiped his hand over his mouth.

Sam didn't immediately respond. She just stared at Anthony, ridiculing him in her mind. She fought the temptation to ask him if he had a second job in the circus. "You told me that your friend needed a job, so I hired her as a favor to you."

Sam was about to retort but switched gears, "I heard some office gossip concerning Tracy's employment."

Sam continued to explain that Tracy needed the job, and in spite of the absences, Tracy was, in fact, dependable. While Sam spoke, she didn't notice that Anthony had removed his glasses and was looking at her with desirous eyes. After Sam concluded her pleas on behalf of Tracy, she headed for the door to leave, but as she placed her hand on the doorknob, Anthony's voice caused her to pause.

"Sam, wait a second."

Sam turned around, hopeful that she had saved her friend's job. Anthony walked over to Sam and placed his hand on her forearm.

"I was certainly going to fire Tracy, but now I'm going to think about it."

Sam's first reaction was the thought, *no this little fat motherfucker don't have his hand on me*. From Sam's facial expression, Anthony got the message; therefore, he promptly removed his hand.

"Sam, I'm not going to pussyfoot with you. I'm going to be straight up. Can I take you to dinner tonight?"

Sam wanted to burst out in laughter, but she managed to contain herself.

"No thank you."

"Why not?"

"I don't eat on Wednesday nights."

Anthony chuckled, admiring Sam's quick wit along with her humor. This increases Anthony's attraction to Sam.

"I thought we could get something to eat and talk about Tracy," said the fat man, raising an inviting eyebrow.

CHARLIE BASSETT JR.

In the past, Anthony had gotten a desperate employee to sleep with him when her job was in peril. Today he felt confident that Sam might be willing to at least have dinner with him to save Tracy's job. Anthony also hoped that after an expensive meal and a little persuasion he just might be able to bed the leggy beauty.

Ready to push the issue, Anthony placed a soft hand upon Sam's shoulder. Again, she hated that she enjoyed the fragrance of his cologne. But she was more repulsed by the skin-to-skin contact.

"Anthony, you know this is inappropriate, don't ever touch me again, thank you."

"Why are you acting like this? I helped you out with getting your friend a job."

"I appreciate that. It's time for me to get back to work. Forget we had this conversation, you're going to do what you're going to do anyway," said, a frustrated Sam as she turned to leave.

Whether Anthony had forgotten Sam's warning or perhaps he was just feeling cocky, whatever the case, Anthony reached out and patted Sam on her back.

"I respect you, Sam. I'll think about Tracy's situation."

The pat on her back caused Sam's mind to swell with rage. She didn't hear the words Anthony had uttered. Sam spun around, almost pivoting like a professional boxer. With a clenched fist, she punched Anthony square in the eye. Anthony grunted in pain as he bent over holding his eye. Sam froze for a moment, realizing fully what she had done.

"You fucking hit me bitch! I'll kick your ass!"

Figuring that Anthony would follow through with his threat when he recovered, Sam wondered if she should follow up with another punch or a kick to the balls. Sam chose neither; she hurried out of Anthony's office. All eyes were on Sam as she headed to her cubicle in a brisk walk. At her cubicle she grabbed her pocketbook and fled the scene.

Five minutes later, Sam sat behind the wheel of her car sweating around her neck and a bit shaken.

"Shit, I'm going to jail," Sam said as she turned the key in the ignition

•••

When Dawn finally emerged from the clinic, her face was taut and her eyes were watery. She climbed into Tracy's Pathfinder and waited for a comment from Tracy. But Tracy remained silent the entire drive home.

•••

A'Man walked down the sidewalk of his block rubbing the butt of the woman on his arm. Both of them were tipsy and horny. The woman giggled like a school girl when A'Man whispered in her ear, promising that the dick she was about to receive would be good and addictive. *It better be*, the woman thought with a grin.

The couple had met two hours earlier at a nearby restaurant. The woman was dining alone when A'Man entered. She was instantly drawn to his good looks.

After a light meal and several drinks—including the obligatory flirting—the woman agreed to go home with A'Man.

Three doors away from A'Man's house, the woman stopped. She pulled him close to her warm body, meeting his lips with a wet kiss. The heat from the woman's body and the kiss heightened A'Man's arousal. He couldn't wait to get her to bed and carry out his promise. If A'Man hadn't been distracted by the kiss, he would've noticed his estranged wife's car parked in front of his house. Mirrar was slumped down in the driver's seat, praying he didn't see her.

A'Man and Mirrar had been separated for over a month, but she wasn't ready to let him go. That was apparent from the many messages a day she left on his voicemail. They had been married for a year. Ironically, today was their anniversary.

Mirrar had been the perfect wife, catering to A'Man's every desire. A'Man, on the other hand, was a serial adulterer, and a sloppy one at that. Each time he had been busted, the same routine transpired; he would be the one to cry, vowing to never be unfaithful again. And although he never attended a session, he suggested marriage counseling, sex therapy, and anything else to keep his fragile marriage together.

A'Man surprised Mirrar a month ago on a warm Thursday night after lovemaking. He climbed out of bed and informed her that their marriage had run its course. He said it was time for them to do their own thing.

After delivering an elegant speech about love, relationships, and the finality of those affairs, A'Man removed his fully-packed suitcase from the closet and left Mirrar sitting naked on the bed, drowning in her tears.

Now, on a night that she thought should be a night of celebration, she was hiding in her car. She hated the role she had adopted—a stalker wife. But she couldn't help herself. When it came to A'Man, she was rendered helpless and her thought process was always irrational.

She had waited in the car for over three hours for A'Man to come home. Her intentions were to persuade him to let her in his house. Once inside, she would make love to him so passionately that he would realize that leaving her was a mistake. They would cry in each other's arms from the pain of their troubles and the joy of their reunion. In the morning, A'Man would pack his belongings and return with her to the house where they once made their home.

That was the plan until Mirrar spotted A'Man approaching with the woman on his arm. Like any optimist, Mirrar held out hope that she could still accomplish her mission because the night was still young.

After A'Man and the woman entered his house, Mirrar stepped out of the car. Mirrar was a beautiful woman, but since the separation, stress had assaulted her appearance. Her hair was long, thick, and unkempt. She had raccoon eyes from lack of sleep, and she had started talking to herself whenever she thought of A'Man.

FRIENDS

Mirrar looked at the downstairs window of A'Man's house, waiting for a light to be turned on. After a moment with no movement of A'Man and the woman's silhouettes, Mirrar turned her attention to the upstairs windows. Five minutes later, with no visible action of the doings inside, Mirrar came to grips with the reality that A'Man and the woman were probably in bed doing the obvious. Mirrar paced back and forth in front of A'Man's house, wrangling with herself concerning her next move.

Inside the house, A'Man hadn't made it to his bedroom before the woman attacked him on the stairs. She snatched his pants down to his ankles. With a strong grip, she ravished his penis, treating him to a blow-job with such intensity that A'Man smacked his palm repeatedly against the wall in sexual rapture.

When they finally made it to the bedroom, their bodies collided onto the bed engaged in a sex feud. They moaned, panted, and even grunted animal noises. Their hearts palpitated while their sweaty bodies clapped a rhythm of a raw sex tune. The woman embedded her nails in A'Man's back as he punished her pelvis with fierce pumping. When the battle was over, the two combatants felt drained of bodily fluids and collapsed on their backs beaming. Not before long, they both fell asleep.

Five hours later, the naked woman awoke with her arm across A'Man's chest. Her eyes were fixed wide with shock and fear as she looked up. Mirrar stood next to the bed staring down at the couple.

"Aaaaah!" The woman screamed.

"Shhh!" Mirrar urged with her finger over her mouth. Mirrar looked frantically at A'Man, who was jolted out of his sleep. He looked at Mirrar as if she was a ghost.

"Hi," Mirrar said in a broken voice.

"What the hell are you doing?" A'Man said as he jumped out of bed searching for his pants.

"Please don't be mad. We need to talk," Mirrar said, looking confused.

While A'Man was slipping on his pants, Mirrar leaned towards the frightened woman, who backed away while wrapping the sheet around her.

"I didn't mean to startle you. I have to tell you something."

The woman held the sheet tightly to her neck as if it could somehow protect her from whatever harm Mirrar had intended for her. A'Man rushed over to Mirrar and seized her by the forearm, ushering her to the door against her struggle.

"Get off of me!"

"How the hell did you get in here?"

"You left the door unlocked."

"You're sick."

"Get off of me! I have to tell you something."

"Ouch!" A'Man yelled as he grabbed his arm, feeling the wetness of blood caused by the knife in Mirrar's hand. A'Man jumped back from her.

For the first time, he saw the blankness in her eyes. He wondered if that sign of craziness had been there when they first met.

"You cut me!"

"It was an accident!"

A'Man found his T-shirt and pressed it against the wound. Mirrar moved quickly towards the terrified woman, but stopped a couple of feet away from her. A'Man wondered what he should do, but he was as much afraid as the woman on the bed.

"Please don't hurt me," said the woman.

"I'm his wife."

"Put down the knife!" A'Man shouted as he calculated the best course of action to take.

"Did he tell you he was married?"

The woman shook her head "no."

"Did he tell you that today is our anniversary? I bought him all the clothes he has?"

The woman cursed herself silently for embarking on this one-night stand. She also hated A'Man for not unarming

FRIENDS

the crazy woman that was in front of her holding the knife like it was a comb.

"I'm going to call the police," A'Man said.

"Call the damn cops!" Mirrar responded.

A'Man was about to race out of the room to phone 911, but the man in him restrained him from abandoning his helpless sex-partner. He thought about charging Mirrar, but fear erased that notion. He decided that diplomacy would be the best option.

"Mirrar, I still care about you. Yes, we can talk. We need to discuss our future. Anything is possible."

"Why is she in your bed if we have a future?"

"I didn't know he was married," the woman said in a meek voice.

"He's a fucking liar! Did he tell you he fucked my sister?"

"No."

A'Man made up his mind that if he or the woman was going to get out of the room without further bloodshed, he had to tackle Mirrar.

"Listen, I just want to leave. Y'all can work out what y'all have to."

"I'm sick of this shit!" Mirrar said while looking at the woman threateningly.

A tear fell from the woman's eyes. A'Man was seconds away from making his move, then in a sudden change of events, Mirrar ran out of the house.

"That bitch is sick...I'm sorry."

The woman jumped off the bed and quickly gathered her clothes. "This is my fault for fucking with a stranger," the woman said as she dressed quickly.

"Can I get your number?" A'Man asked.

"Are you kidding?" the woman said as she was rushing out of the room.

A'Man sat on edge of the bed, dumbfounded as to what had just occurred.

•••

11

Dawn's apartment was small but opulent. A trace of frankincense scented the air. Lining the walls were photographs and painting of African safaris. Stationed throughout the apartment was African pottery. But the reference to Dawn's ancestral motherland was a façade, because her only religion or culture pertained to U.S. currency.

Dawn looked withdrawn as she lay on the sofa underneath a green, black, and red hand-knitted blanket. Across from her sat Tracy, who looked a bit detached herself.

Sam stood in front of the full-length mirror posing and preening her hair that fell past her shoulders. Standing by Sam's side was Tracy's daughter Tammy, who was joyfully imitating Sam's every move.

"No honey, put one hand on your hip and with your other hand flick your hair like this," Sam said as she demonstrated how a diva should grace a mirror.

"Am I doing right?"

"Yes, honey," Sam said.

With a childlike voice Tracy said, "Aunt Sam, I didn't know you were so conceited."

"You didn't, honey?"

Tammy patted Sam on her leg to get her attention, "Aunt Sam, when I grow up will I be pretty like you?"

"Yes, honey, and if you drink your milk, your little tits will be as big as mine are."

Sam cupped her 36Ds and rocked them upward. Tammy smiled embarrassingly as she glanced back at her mother, who, too, was smiling. Although there were smiles all around, Dawn's smile was really an upside-down frown due to the complex she had about her own small breasts.

Even though Dawn was, by far, the most successful among her friends, she often measured herself against their good looks and shapely physiques. Dawn wasn't an ugly

Betty, but secretly inside she felt like one, so she compensated by dressing in expensive clothing and jewelry.

As Dawn and Tracy continued to watch Tammy play diva with Sam, their minds roved back to the events from earlier that day. Dawn wondered if the baby she aborted was a girl or a boy. Tracy stressed over whether or not she still had a job, and if she didn't have a job, she wondered how she would pay her bills.

"Tammy, that's enough playing. Go in your Aunt Dawn's room and watch TV," Tracy said in a voice that preempted any objection from her daughter.

Tammy was flabbergasted, as any child would be whose ordered to stop having fun without an explanation. Although Tammy looked deflated, she promptly left the living room.

"Sam, did Anthony actually say that he was going to fire me?"

"Like I told you when we got here, after what I did, we both are fired."

"What if he presses criminal charges against you?" Dawn asked as she sat up.

"Fuck that pussy! What's he going to tell the police? A woman kicked my ass."

"He won't go to the cops. That would be too embarrassing," Tracy said.

"You could file sexual harassment," Dawn suggested.

"The way I see it, Anthony wanted a piece of my ass but I got a piece of his, so we're even."

"If he does decide to press charges, I could represent you."

"Imagine that," Sam scoffed.

"I'm a lawyer."

"You are a civil attorney, or should I say, rookie lawyer who only passed the bar six months ago. You're not sending me to jail. Shit, you'd probably open the door to the fact that I hit him without probable cause.

Dawn felt insulted but displayed a poker face.

13

"Damn, I needed that job. I have all these bills," Tracy said.

"You shouldn't have taken off from work. You knew you couldn't afford it," Sam said.

Although Sam looked at Tracy when she spoke, Sam's words were directed at Dawn. Dawn felt the blow, but she remained silent and continued to hold her poker face.

"Dawn, can you get Tracy a job at your firm?"

"Uh…I just started there…I don't know how the partners would respond, you know --"

"No, I don't know," said Sam.

Realizing that Sam was attempting to start an argument with Dawn, Tracy felt the need to intercede, "I don't know anything about being a lawyer. I can't type."

As Tracy continued to make excuses for Dawn, Sam's anger grew.

"Dawn, did you tell Dave you got an abortion?" Sam said, looking at Dawn through the reflection in the mirror.

The question caught both Dawn and Tracy by surprise. Sam, however, remained impassive as she awaited a response. Dawn glared at her friend of twenty years with more contempt than she had for anyone before in her life.

"Well, did you?" Sam asked heartlessly.

Tracy was about to intervene but didn't because she too, wanted an answer to the question.

"This is my body and what I do with it is neither Dave's business, nor yours, or anyone else's."

"Bitch, who are you talking to like that?"

"I'm just stating a fact."

"Fuck your stinking facts!"

"Come on y'all, calm down," Tracy said.

"I'm calm. Sam's the one who's being disrespectful and cussing like a sailor."

"Fuck you."

"Fuck you, too."

Although Sam had no intentions on getting physical, she took a threatening step towards Dawn. Dawn jumped to her feet. Tracy centered herself between her two friends.

"Cool out! What's wrong with y'all?"

"This bitch thinks she better than somebody, little fraud, fake- ass bitch with all this African shit around here. If you want to go back to Africa, catch a fucking plane, you got the money."

"Jealous?"

Sam was irate. To keep herself from putting her hands on Dawn, Sam walked across the room.

"You've been jealous of me since we were in the seventh grade."

"Ain't nobody jealous of your ugly ass."

Ugly! The utterance of the word hurt like a hard punch to the jaw. Dawn's hurt was apparent on her face. She combed her brain for a response that would be as hurtful to Sam as the one Sam had delivered to her.

"At least I never fucked two brothers."

Anger distorted Sam's face and Dawn loved it. Seeing Dawn smirking added to Sam's rage.

"I'm going to kick your ass!" yelled Sam.

Sam smacked a piece of pottery off the table. It crashed to the floor and broke. Dawn was stunned speechless as she marched toward an embattled Sam, but Tracy restrained Dawn.

"Let that bitch go, she knows she'll get her ass kicked!"

"Let me go, Tracy!"

"No!"

Tammy ran into the room looking frightened. Tammy's presence brought calm to the room.

"Tammy, go back in the bedroom," Tracy ordered.

"No, Tammy, you're about to go home," said Dawn, "I'm tired and it's time for y'all to leave."

Sam grabbed her jacket and pocketbook and stormed out of the house.

"All of this wasn't necessary," Tracy said as she gathered her and Tammy's jackets.

"She started it."

"It doesn't matter, y'all are family."

"Whatever."

After exchanging goodbyes, Tracy and Tammy left. Tracy was surprised to see Sam waiting outside.

"I'm going to get that bitch. I didn't know they were brothers, and I was sixteen at the time."

"You don't have to explain nothing to me. The argument between you and Dawn is over. Just go home, I'll call you later."

"I'm sorry Tammy, but your Aunt Sam doesn't take mess from anyone."

Sam embraced Tracy. Afterwards, the women hopped in their cars and drove off.

Ten minutes after leaving Dawn's place, Tracy pulled her Pathfinder to a stop in front of her house. She picked up her cell phone from the passenger seat and smiled as she read the text message from Rob stating, "See U soon."

As Tracy and Tammy walked towards their house, Tracy stopped when she saw the silhouette of a person sitting on her porch. When the person stood and his identity came into focus, Tracy sighed at the sight of Tammy's father Steve, who was now walking towards them.

"You can't keep my daughter away from me!"

"Who gave you my address?"

As Steve bent over towards Tammy, Tracy positioned Tammy behind her.

"Hi, Tammy. How are you doing baby?"

Tammy waved hello shyly.

"Don't speak to her."

Tracy picked up Tammy and attempted to head towards the door, but Steve blocked Tracy's path.

"Move!"

"I just want to see her," Steve said pleadingly.

Tracy sat Tammy on her feet; then she stepped to Steve.

"Now you want to see her! What did you say when I was pregnant, 'She ain't my daughter.'"

Steve looked hurt and embarrassed as he shot a quick look at Tammy to assess her reaction. But Tammy showed no emotions. It was as if she had witnessed her parents arguing like this before.

"I only said that stuff because --"

"Because shit! And when Tammy needed pampers and formula, what did you say, 'Tell her father to buy it.'

"I'm sorry."

"Fuck your sorry."

"I'm not going to be arguing with you about seeing Tammy. I'm going to court."

"Come on, Tammy."

While Tracy took Tammy's hand and proceeded towards the house, Steve grabbed Tracy by her arm.

From across the street, Tracy's friend Rob was parking his car and witnessing the encounter. After parking, Rob rushed over.

"Yo, get your hands off of her."

"Who the fuck is you," Steve said, releasing his grip from Tracy.

Tracy looked relieved to see Rob, who kissed her on her cheek, to the dismay of Steve.

"Rob, this is the sperm donor I told you about. It's okay , wait for me in the house."

"No," Rob said.

Although Tracy had asked Rob to go in the house, she didn't object when he refused.

"Dude, this is none of your business," Steve said.

Before Rob could respond, Tracy said, "File whatever papers you want, but don't ever come to my house again."

"I am going to court!"

"Tracy, take Tammy in the house. I want to talk to this guy for a minute."

Without hesitation, Tracy took Tammy in the house, sat her on the couch, and with a stern finger ordered Tammy not to move. Tracy rushed over to the open door and stood there watching the men outside.

"My name is Rob."

"Steve."

Rob extended his hand and Steve shook it. Tracy grimaced as she shook her head wondering why Rob was being cordial with the enemy.

"Listen, Steve, I would never come between a man and his child I have a son. Although he doesn't live with me, I take care of him," said Rob emphatically, "Now Tracy is my lady."

Although Tracy had not made any commitments to Rob, hearing him refer to her as his lady brought a smile to her face. Steve's expression said he could care less.

"Like I said, it's not my intentions to keep you away from Tammy, but Tracy told me that when she was pregnant you denied Tammy, and even after the blood test you still didn't step up. And she didn't even try to get child support."

"She was running around the fucking street like a smut," Steve said barely audible so that Tracy wouldn't over hear.

Rob looked angry as he thought, *Dawn told me she was a good girl and wasn't in the streets.* A few seconds later, Rob came to his senses, realizing what Steve was trying to do.

"I don't care about her past, and this is about a child."

"This is between me and Tracy."

"Well, I'm putting myself in the middle of it."

Rob took a step towards Steve, invading his space. But Steve wasn't the least bit threatened.

"I'm just going on what my woman told me."

Again, Tracy smiled as her heart rate increased, anticipating a fight.

"This is what's going to happen. I'm going to speak with Tracy about making arrangements for you to see Tammy. We'll take things slow."

Tracy was about to yell, "Hell no," but she remained silent.

"I respect what you're saying, but I should be having this conversation with the mother of my child. I haven't seen my daughter in two years."

Rob placed his hands over his face in frustration. He looked back over his shoulder at Tracy who mouthed the words, "Fuck him."

"Yo, was you locked up for those two years that you didn't see Tammy?"

"No."

"So what the fuck prevented you from seeing your daughter or giving Tracy money for her?"

"I don't have to explain shit to you --Tracy, get the fuck out here!" Steve yelled.

"It's time for you to step."

"I don't have to go anywhere."

"You're right."

Rob turned slightly as if he was about to walk away, but he didn't. He clenched his fist and swung a haymaker that caught Steve on the chin. The punch was weak, but it still caused Steve to stumble backwards. Before Steve could get his feet under him, Rob followed up with a three piece two jabs and a straight right hand to Steve's face, causing him to take a knee.

Tracy, who had left the doorway and was now standing on the steps, looked happily excited. Tracy clenched her fist, wishing it was her delivering the ass whipping to the enemy.

Rob was about to finish Steve, but somehow Steve recovered just enough to sprint to his car. For a moment, Rob was fearful that Steve had run to retrieve a weapon, but when Steve sped off in his car, Rob was relieved.

•••

When Sam left from Dawn's apartment, she was nettled and didn't want to go directly home, so she decided that she needed a drink to take the edge off. As she headed to a familiar sports bar she frequented, she spotted a liquor store along the way and pulled into the parking lot.

While Sam was at the counter paying for a pint of Jameson Irish Whiskey, A'Man entered the store. The sound of the door opening caused Sam to look in that direction. At that instant, Sam and A'Man's eyes met and locked for a moment. The store clerk broke the connection when he offered Sam her change.

As A'Man walked towards Sam at the counter, he checked her out from behind. Sam didn't have to look back to know that he was digging her. But Sam was unfazed by his staring. She was well aware that she was a magnet for men and had been since she was fifteen. She had become accustomed to being hit on; in fact, sometimes it was annoying for her.

"How are you doing?" A'Man asked.

"Okay," Sam responded.

"Can I speak with you a moment?"

Sam knew what he wanted to talk about, and it wasn't to discuss politics. A voice in her head said he's cute, so talk to him. Although A'Man's good looks piqued her interest, Sam just gave him a polite smile and left the store. Even though he had just gotten shot down, A'Man was unaffected because of his King Kong size ego.

As she drove home, Sam thought about the encounter for a moment. Afterwards, she simply put it out of her head like she had done with all the other pursuers before him.

Sam parked her car down the street from her house. She picked up the pint of whiskey and drank half of the bottle, screwed back on the top, and placed the bottle underneath the driver's seat. Not ready to go into the house, Sam sat behind the wheel for a few minutes longer thinking, *what a life.*

When Sam finally entered her house, she was accosted by her husband Andrew.

"Where were you at?"

"Over your niece's house."

"No you weren't. I spoke with Dawn," Andrew said, lying. He had hoped to catch Sam in a lie herself.

"Yes, I was," said Sam as she picked up the phone, "you can ask her."

"Do you know what time it is?"

Sam glanced at her watch, "Nine fifteen," Sam said meekly.

"You know I have to go to work soon and you're over Dawn's house running your damn mouth."

Sam lowered her head like a child that was ready to endure the scolding from a parent.

"You were drinking. I can smell it from here. You're always over Dawn's house drinking and bullshitting. One of these days I'm going to --"

Andrew's words were cut short by the sound of rumbling from upstairs.

"Stop that damn running," Sam shouted as she looked up at the ceiling.

"Don't scream at them. If you were home doing your job the kids wouldn't be out of control."

Andrew placed his hand on his hips and stared at Sam, wondering if she had ever cheated on him. Sam had been through the routine too many times. She knew exactly what her husband was thinking before he said the words.

"Sam?"

"What?" Sam asked annoyingly.

"You better not be cheating."

"Why would you do this? I'm not fucking around, and you know it. You always accuse me. Are you fucking somebody?"

"Who the fuck are you cursing at?"

Sam figured Andrew was looking for a fight before he left for work, so she chose her words carefully.

"I'm sorry for my language baby. I had a bad day. My supervisor made some inappropriate comments, we got into it, and I got fired."

Sam saw the sweat forming on Andrew's nose and forehead, something that happened every time he got angry. Sam's getting fired wasn't the fruit of his anger because Andrew didn't want her working in the first place. Andrew's income was sufficient enough to provide for his family. What caused Andrew's anger was the possibility that a man

CHARLIE BASSETT JR.

may have disrespected his wife. Sam knew her husband and his thoughts, so she wanted to kill the issue on the spot.

"I started the whole thing."

After Andrew studied Sam's eyes and was satisfied that she had spoken the truth, the perspiration on his face seemed to evaporate, and Sam was thankful, for Anthony's sake.

Outside of her home, Sam was a rock, but in her husband's presence she was fragile.

"We'll talk about this when I come home. Get your ass upstairs and tell the kids to stop running."

Andrew shook his head as he took one last look at Sam before he left. As Sam walked up the stairs slowly and defeated, she wondered how much more of this she could take.

"Mommy, Rita hit me," Sam's youngest daughter whined.

Sam rushed up the stairs and grabbed Rita violently by the collar.

"Y'all better stop or I'm going to fuck all of y'all up."

Later that night, Sam lay in bed alone reminiscing about the first time she had met her husband.

It was twelve years ago. Dawn had invited Sam to a cookout, but Sam declined due to previous plans to go away with her cousin. But at the last moment, Sam's cousin canceled, so Sam caught a ride over to the park where Dawn's family was barbecuing.

While Sam was sitting on a bench eating a cheeseburger and talking with Dawn, she noticed a man staring at her. He was handsome, with dangerous eyes, and ironically, he was wearing a wife-beater t-shirt which showed off his upper body build.

Sam whispered to Dawn that there was a guy who kept staring at her. Dawn looked over and said that's my Uncle Andrew who just moved back into the city. Moments later, Andrew walked over and sat next to Sam.

22

Sam replayed the encounter in her mind and uttered word for word the exchange.

"What's up y'all?"

"Hey, Uncle Andrew."

Sam remembered that for the first time in her life she was lost for words.

"Can I have a bite?" Andrew asked, referring to Sam's burger. Sam was caught off guard. She smiled as she remembered how she extended the burger to him.

"Uncle Andrew, leave my girlfriend alone and get your own food. Plus, she's only seventeen and you're ten years older than she is."

"I want some of hers...Can I have some?"

Sam didn't respond. She looked at Dawn who shook her head "no."

"Uncle Andrew, leave us alone. We were talking."

"Alright."

Andrew stood from the bench and touched Sam on her shoulder before he walked away. Sam remembered that his touch felt like fire. The fire that didn't burn, but incited passion.

During that day, Andrew didn't say a word to Sam, but he kept staring. When she had went home and lay in her bed, she could still feel his dangerous eyes upon her, and she wasn't sure how she felt about it.

Two weeks after the park encounter, Andrew showed up at Sam's high school and offered her a ride home. Sam hesitantly got into the passenger seat. Twenty minutes later, as Sam sat in Andrew's apartment, she wondered what would Dawn think if she knew where she was at.

Although Sam wasn't a virgin, she felt like one as she lay naked and ready to receive Andrew. When he stuck it in, she gasped from his size and wrapped her arms around his neck, choking him. An hour later when they were finished, they just lay there recuperating without saying a word.

That day changed Sam's life. She was introduced to her first drink by Andrew. He was the recipient of her first blow job, and she had her pussy eaten by him. Although she had sex three times before, this was the first time she had made love.

Sam and Andrew snuck around successfully for three months until they were discovered. Dawn was furious and jealous, because Andrew was her favorite uncle and she didn't think someone Sam's age was appropriate for him.

A year after meeting, Sam and Andrew were married at the displeasure of both of their families. But they didn't care, because they were in love.

In the beginning years, the marriage was wonderful, but then Andrew developed insecurity towards his beautiful young wife who couldn't walk down the street without getting hit on.

After five years of marriage, Sam finally became pregnant with her first child. Two more followed, and that's when the real problems began.

Because Sam had taken so long to conceive, Andrew had doubts about whether he was the children's father. After the humiliation of having to take a blood test to prove her truthfulness, Sam never looked at Andrew the same or had the same passion when they made love. Andrew, in turn, became even more jealous. So year after year Sam secretly suffered and endured verbal and physical abuse.

As Sam lay in the bed, a tear fell from her eye. She wished things could go back to how they were before the abuse. Then out of the blue, she thought about A'Man and how he looked at her. And for the first time in her marriage, the idea that another man desired her turned Sam on. She thought, *what was wrong with having a friendly conversation with a handsome man?* Then reality hit. She knew that if Andrew found out that she was even thinking about another man, somebody would get hurt, namely her. So Sam accepted her life and fell asleep

• • •

FRIENDS

After the thrashing Rob had given to Steve, Tracy felt that Rob deserved a treat. She put Tammy to bed, took a shower, and set the mood in her bedroom for a night of sex. Tracy's bedroom was pitch black. The soft music played just loud enough for a person to be heard without the speaker raising their voice.

Tracy instructed Rob to stand in the center of the room and remain silent. With slow hands, she removed his clothes, tossing them in the corner of the room. Thereafter, she sat on the edge of the bed, leaving Rob standing in the dark for a long minute. Just when Rob was beginning to feel awkward, something soft tickled his balls. Rob flinched with excitement. His initial thought was that Tracy was using a feather to stimulate him. He was wrong. It was cotton.

Rob's penis shot forward. Tracy stroked him gently with her free hand. Rob's chest expanded and deflated rapidly from the inhaling and exhaling of the deep breaths he took as Tracy worked wonders with the cotton ball between her fingers.

As the sensation intensified, the moistness and softness of Tracy's lips laid a kiss on the side of Rob's penis. He swallowed hard. Anticipating a blow job, his dick was yearning for it as Tracy's tongue wiped across a protruding vein. Rob couldn't wait as he reached out in the dark, finding Tracy's head and pulling it towards him. But Tracy removed his hands and placed them at his side.

"Patience," she whispered.

The cotton ball that had tickled Rob's balls was now slowly descending on the small of his back and stopping at the crack of his ass. Tracy squeezed Rob's butt cheek and moved her index finger slowly towards the center. *Rob's whole body clenched to prevent any possible entry. You're not sticking anything in me. I'm not that freaky.* When Rob had tightened, Tracy smiled, because she was certainly going to test him with her finger, if his body language suggested that he was into that.

Tracy smacked Rob on his ass cheek and said, "Relax."

25

Like a playful pussycat, Tracy crawled between Rob's spread legs with her head rubbing against his inner thighs as she passed through. Tracy was now on her knees before him. *Finally*, Rob thought as he prepared himself for the long awaited warmth of Tracy's mouth.

But Tracy's mouth didn't go where Rob had expected. She kissed his inner thighs again, massaging them while lifting her head underneath his penis, moving her head from side-to-side, ever so slight. The sensation of Tracy's hair intertwining with his penis intensified Rob's hunger to be inside Tracy in one area or another. Again, he grabbed her head to guide her to his penis, but again, she placed his hands to his side and patted them as an indication to stay put.

Tracy rose slowly and licked Rob around his pubic hair from right to left. Her tongue traveled upwards to his bellybutton. Soon, her tongue found his chest, his nipples, his neck, and ultimately his mouth. She kissed him hard. Her tongue dominating his in a snake fight. All the while, rubbing her body hard against his penis. The friction produced pre-cum that she felt on her thigh.

Suddenly, without warning, Tracy disengaged and pushed Rob to the bed. She mounted him in the 69 position. Rob smiled as he inhaled the clean smell of Dove soap coming from Tracy's vagina. Rob loved the smell of Dove soap.

As if they were starving, the pair devoured each other in an eating frenzy. The scene was as if they were in a contest to see who was best. If their moans and heavy grunts were any indication, it was a tie.

After they both reached their climaxes, it wasn't long before their bodies craved for more.

Tracy lay on her back and placed her legs on Rob's shoulders and whispered in his ear to go slow. Her wet tongue followed the words spoken into Rob's ear. She was so aggressive that he believed that she was trying to drive her tongue down his ear canal.

As Rob made slow love to Tracy, she whispered that she was very ticklish and told him to tickle her feet and ribs.

Rob did as instructed and Tracy went exotic, squirming uncontrollably. She laughed herself to tears. She screamed, moaned, bit Rob on his hard chest, and choked him.

"Harder Motherfucker!"

Rob increased the tickling and his pumping. He panted heavily with each powerful thrust while Tracy grabbed his butt, wedging him to her. Suddenly, Tracy's body jerked as she reached an orgasm. When they were finally wiped out, they lay there sweaty, out of breath, and fulfilled.

"What are you thinking?" Rob asked.

"Nothing really, just catching my breath."

Although Tracy had spoken the truth about catching her breath, she lied about her thoughts, because she was thinking that she had found her husband.

CHAPTER

2

As usual, Dawn was the first lawyer to arrive at the prestigious law firm where she worked. With childlike admiration, she looked at the senior partner's nameplates on their doors, promising herself that one day she would also be among the elite.

After a quick spell of daydreaming about a prosperous future, Dawn sat at her desk and started proofreading a legal brief. But it wasn't before long that her focus began to tail off. Several times she placed the brief in a legal folder, intending on viewing it a later time, only to pick up the brief moments later and resume reading.

Dawn's focus was disrupted by thoughts of the argument she had last night with Sam. No matter how hard she tried, she couldn't shake the question that Sam asked—whether or not Dawn had told Dave about the abortion. While Dawn was lost in her thoughts, she didn't notice that a senior partner, Mr. Hall, had walked up and stood behind her.

"A penny for your thoughts." Mr. Hall asked. Dawn was initially startled, until she took a backward glance and saw who it was behind her. She gave Mr. Hall a slight smile, and then she looked forward with a straight face.

"My mind was a million miles away."

"I noticed... I see we're the first ones in the office, as usual."

"Yes. I was just proofing the Johnson's brief" Dawn said as she picked up the brief, holding it in her hands.

FRIENDS

To take a closer look at the brief, Mr. Hall leaned over Dawn while brushing his chest against her shoulder.

"I'll take a closer look at it when you're done", he said, standing erect.

"Okay."

"You smell good this morning, Dawn. What is that fragrance?"

"Thank you."

"Oh, how was the doctor's visit yesterday."

"It was just a six-month checkup. Everything is fine."

"Good to hear."

There was a moment of awkward silence as Dawn needlessly organized papers on her desk.

"I called you last night," Mr. Hall said.

"I was a little stressed, so I turned off my phone and went to bed early."

"Stress comes with the territory," said Mr. Hall as he placed his sixty-four-year-old, wrinkled hands on Dawn's shoulders, "I missed you."

Dawn looked a bit uncomfortable. Her body tensed as Mr. Hall massaged her shoulders.

"You are extremely tight."

"I'm just going through a lot right now", Dawn said as she stood.

She picked up a legal file and walked over to the file cabinet.

"I don't like it when you do that here. Someone might see."

"That's nothing to concern yourself with. Let me worry about that, okay?'

Mr. Hall stepped behind Dawn and placed a kiss on her cheek, "I really need to see you, baby."

Dawn's eyes darted about nervously as she sighed inside. Just when she was about to speak, someone outside the office called for Mr. Hall. Dawn prayed that the person didn't see how close he had been to her.

"Well, duty calls," Mr. Hall said before whispering, "I'll speak with you later."

CHARLIE BASSETT JR.

After he left, Dawn sat at her desk and placed her hands over her face. She was silently asking herself how did she let things go this far, especially, with a white man more than twice her age.

Once Dawn had shaken the incident with Mr. Hall out of her mind, she resumed her thoughts of Sam's question. And for whatever reason, Dawn was beginning to think that Sam had a point. Dave should know about the abortion.

Dawn figured that if she held this secret from Dave, it could come back to haunt her. So against that little voice in her head that said don't tell him, Dawn picked up the phone and called Dave and asked him to meet her for lunch

...

Earlier that day, Tracy awoke just before the crack of dawn to the shrill sounds of alley cats fighting, mating, or whatever else they did during the early morning hours. Tracy yawned, outstretched her arms, and smiled as she recalled the sexual satisfaction she achieved last night thanks to "Sugar Dick." That was her new pet name for Rob after last's night performance. Tracy turned on her side and watched Rob as he slept peacefully.

Dawn had introduced Tracy to Rob one night while they were at a club. At their introduction, Tracy was cold toward Rob, but after the urging of Dawn, Tracy exchanged numbers with the pretty-boy against her better judgment.

Tracy usually didn't date men who thought that they looked better than her, and she assumed Rob was this type. In her experience, men with Rob's killer looks were trouble. They always brought drama—namely females—from the past or present, and surely to come in the future.

As Tracy watched Rob sleep, she asked herself, *is it too soon to ask him to move in?* No! She answered the question without hesitation. *Shit, I want to marry him*, she almost said aloud.

Tracy glanced at the time. It was an hour before she needed to get up and get ready for work. Then she frowned, remembering that she probably didn't have a job, no thanks to Sam. Tracy had conveniently forgotten that it was her absences that kicked off the whole fiasco.

As Tracy continued to gaze at Rob, *she thought, damn, he even looks good in his sleep.* Tracy began to feel horny. She ducked underneath the covers and found his limped penis, which was small without the fill of blood transforming in to "Sugar Dick." As she toyed with his "Whip-her stick" in her hand, tongue, and mouth, Rob awoke groggily. Before he could gather his mental thoughts, his penis understood what was happening as it sprung to life like a balloon. After she got him off, she wiped her mouth and eased up into his arms.

"You like that?"

"Yes."

Rob kissed Tracy on the lips and nibbled on her fingers as he stared into her gleaming eyes. She held his glance for a moment before lowering her eyes shyly. *I'm falling fast,* she thought as she stared at the hair on his chest.

"I love you."

The three words slid down Tracy's ear canal and landed at the center of her heart. She was speechless. Shocked. He had taken her by surprise. Tracy knew how she felt about Rob, but she wasn't quite sure how deep he felt about her. Now she did, and she was overjoyed by his words. However, instincts told her to hold her composure. But it was difficult, because her eyes revealed that she was a woman in love, and Rob saw it.

"I mean it. I don't want to be with nobody else but you. Do you believe I know what I want?"

"Yes."

"I think I should move in."

"Okay."

For a moment, neither one of them said another word. They just gazed at each other, letting their eyes speak. As the silent seconds passed, all Tracy could think of is that she loved this man and couldn't wait to call and thank Dawn for the hookup.

When the time came to end their morning intimacy, the couple rose from the bed. Tracy told Rob to shower first. As he washed his face, blinding himself with a thick lather of soap, Tracy stepped into the shower.

Twenty minutes later, Tracy finally managed to pull herself away from Rob. She got Tammy dressed and fixed breakfast for her extended family.

While Tracy and Tammy were sitting at the kitchen table, Rob entered. He kissed Tracy on her forehead and walked over to Tammy. He leaned over as if was going to kiss her on her forehead, but he surprised her by tickling her.

As Tammy squirmed and laughed, Tracy watched and thought about how Rob had tickled and fucked her last night into an orgasm.

"Okay, Rob, that's enough."

Rob took a seat across from Tracy.

"I left money on the table for the babysitter and something for you."

"Thank you."

That was it. The deal-sealer. Tracy had no doubts about it. Rob was, indeed, her future husband. After they concluded breakfast, Tracy walked Rob to the door.

"I'll see you to night. Oh, I might be late if I do overtime," Rob said.

While they were locked in a kiss, the front door opened. In walked Tracy's 18-year-old cousin Joann, who was also the babysitter.

"Okay, that's enough. It's a child in the house," Joann said as she playfully squeezed herself between the two lovers, thereby separating them.

"Yeah, we both have to get to work," Rob said, kissing Tracy on the cheek.

"Have a good day," Tracy said.

Tracy had thought for a moment to tell Rob about the incident between Sam and Anthony, but she decided to tell him later when he came home from work.

FRIENDS

"I'll see you tonight, baby. Bye, Joann," Rob said.

"See you," Tracy said in a sexy voice.

"Bye," Joann uttered.

After Rob left, Joann bragged to Tracy about the new, wonderful, older man in her life. Tracy added how happy she was with Rob, even confessing that she wanted to marry him.

Joann looked surprised as she said, "I'm so happy for you."

After making small talk with Joann for a couple minutes longer, Tracy left for work.

"Cousin Joann, are we going to exercise like the lady on TV?" Tammy asked.

"Don't we always, baby girl?" Joann said as she gave Tammy a wet kiss on her cheek.

Tammy smiled. Joann grabbed a workout DVD and placed it in the player and turned on the TV.

Joann, who was clad in sweatpants and t-shirt, placed Tammy next to her and began following the high-intensity aerobic exercise performed by the instructor on the TV screen.

After ten minutes of trying to keep up with Joann, Tammy looked worn out as she bent over, placing her hands on her knees.

"I'm tired."

"You can't stop if you want to get in shape and be beautiful like me."

So with tired little legs, Tammy made a sloppy attempt to follow the workout routine as best she could. Ten minutes later, Joann carried in her arms a snoring Tammy to her bed and tucked her in. Tammy would be sleep for hours.

Joann took a hot shower. When she was finished, she wrapped a towel around her curvaceous body and walked into Tracy's bedroom. Joann opened Tracy's panties drawer and removed a Victoria Secret negligee. Without a second thought, she let the towel drop to the floor and slipped on her cousin's undergarment.

...

In another household, Sam awoke with Andrew asleep next to her. She looked at him and rolled her eyes in disgust. *He is becoming unbearable.* Andrew had come home three hours earlier with an attitude and a hard-on. Sam loathed the fact that she had to put up with his shit and have sex with him whenever he wanted.

Refusing Andrew's sexual advances was equal to an act of treason against the state in Andrew's eyes. On one occasion, Andrew had initiated foreplay and Sam decided to test the waters by walking away from his embrace, complaining of a headache. Andrew hit the roof with anger. He accused Sam of sleeping with everyone from the mailman to the president. Andrew quoted religious texts concerning a wife's duty to her husband in the bed. He spewed out obscenities. The harshest was calling Sam a stink-pussy bitch. Finally, he threatened to put her in the hospital with an injury far worse than a headache.

To stop his tirade, Sam rubbed his crotch area and told him to come on. It was lost on Andrew that Sam wasn't pumping back during sex.

As Sam stared at a snoring Andrew, she thought, *I could get him now in his sleep.* Fear chased her murderous thought into hiding. With a feeling of despair, she climbed quietly out of bed, showered, and then fixed breakfast for the children before sending them off to school.

Done with her morning chores, Sam reclined on the sofa watching *The Price is Right.* Even though she hated her job, she missed it already. It was far better than guessing the price of soap powder and dreading Andrew waking up hollering and screaming just because he had a mouth. Sam told herself that she had to find another job soon.

"Damn, Tracy!" Sam said, blaming Tracy for her current predicament.

Bored with hearing, "Come on down. You're the next contestant on the Price is Right," Sam turned off the television, grabbed her pocketbook and car keys, and dashed out the door. She hopped in her car and headed to the supermarket that was down the street from the liquor store. She was about to stop for a pint but changed her mind.

While Sam pushed the food cart down the produce-section aisle, she saw a sight up ahead that stopped her in her tracks. It was A'Man carrying a food basket and heading in her direction.

Does my hair look tight? Sam surprised herself with the thought. As A'Man closed in, he recognized Sam. His spirited eyes indicated that he was happy to see her again.

"Didn't I see you at another store last night?" A'Man said while flashing a murderous smile.

"Yeah."

"You know we bumped into each other again for a reason."

Sam hesitated and debated whether to respond or walk away. That voice in her head said, *what's wrong with a friendly conversation?*

"And what reason is that?" Sam asked.

Another voice said, *you're crossing the line, girl!*

"So we could get to know one another. From these two chance meetings, it's obvious we both live near here and should become friends."

Player, Player, Player. Girl, walk away!

"It was nice talking to you, but I'm married."

Now he will say, okay, you take care.

"Many people are married."

"But I'm happily married."

"My name is A'Man," A'Man said cockily as he ignored the brush off.

"A'Man?"

"Yeah. It's capital A, apostrophe, and a regular M-A-N."

"That's different."

Why are you still talking to him? You're married, she silently asked herself.

"What's your name?"

Girl, lie!

"Diana," Sam said with hesitation.

"I live two blocks over. Do you live around here?"

Now it's definitely time to leave! Sam told herself with authority. Before she could obey her thoughts, she heard a familiar voice from behind.

"Hey, Sam."

Sam turned around, surprised to see a mutual acquaintance of her and Andrew's.

"Hey," Sam said while attempting not to sound as guilty as she looked.

"Well, thank you," Sam said as she turned to A'Man, letting him know with her eyes that the conversation was over.

A'Man smiled at the two women and walked away. Both married women's eyes followed him down the aisle, formulating their own fantasies in their cheating minds.

"Who was that?"

"I don't know. He handed me something from the upper shelf."

The woman gave Sam a snicker when she glanced into Sam's cart but didn't see anything from the produce section. Sam felt busted. She wanted to gash out the eyes of the woman who was too observant for her own good.

But Sam kept her cool. She pleasantly chatted with the woman for a moment before walking away angry with herself.

As Sam drove home, all she could think of was the possibility of the woman blabbing to Andrew about seeing Sam at the supermarket talking to this cute guy. Sam was so paranoid and afraid, she selfishly wished that the woman would kneel over and die at that very minute, just so she could never reveal to Andrew what she had witnessed this morning

• • •

FRIENDS

In spite of the cool temperature, Dawn sweated underneath her armpits and around her collar as she stood outside her office building. She was waiting for her boyfriend Dave, who was ten minutes late. His tardiness started to worry Dawn. Dave was never late for anything, no matter how important or insignificant the affair was.

Was it possible that, in her anger, Sam ratted to Dave about the abortion? Dawn wondered.

"Sam wouldn't do that," Dawn uttered just above a whisper.

While she waited, Dawn rehearsed in her mind several alternatives as to how to confess to Dave about the abortion. She favored the career excuse. She would tell Dave that she did it because of their careers.

Like Dawn, Dave himself was an attorney, and had been for the past three years. He was five years her senior and he had no children. In spite of the fact that he was a bit bourgeois, he was genuinely an okay guy.

Dawn loved and respected him; however, she wasn't in love with him. This wouldn't prevent her from marrying him. When she, Tracy, and Sam would discuss the situation, Dawn would quote Tina Turner, "What's love got to do with it?" Dawn also would declare, "We will have a marriage of convenience."

Dawn glanced at her watch as a cool breeze swept across her face. Whether it was the breeze, or Dave's tardiness taking its toll, Dawn abandoned her original plan on how she would break the news to him.

Her mind went into overdrive. *Nothing good can come from telling him. What he doesn't know won't hurt him. What if he leaves you for your honesty? He may become violent upon hearing the news! He just might be understanding.*

"Excuse me, do you have the time?" A passerby asked, interrupting Dawn's thoughts.

"A quarter past twelve."

"Thank you."

As Dawn watched the passerby proceed away, she spotted Dave up the block walking briskly towards her. The closer he got, she could see the white of his teeth from the radiant smile he wore. He waved to Dawn. She perked up and waved back.

After seeing his smile, Dawn settled her dilemma concerning the abortion. She would simply keep it a secret. It would be another secret she carried, like the affair with Mr. Hall, and the one night stand with the cab driver with green eyes and Western European accent.

"Hey, baby."

Dave gave Dawn a kiss.

"I'm sorry I'm late. The judge--"

"It's okay. I just got here myself."

As Dave listened to Dawn, he saw the troubled look on her face, so he touched her cheek with the back of his hand.

"What's wrong?"

"Huh?"

"You look like something is troubling you."

"I'm good. Just thinking about the brief I'm preparing... Let's go. I'm hungry."

Dave placed his arm around Dawn's shoulders. Together they headed down the busy street.

"It's getting cold," Dave said, shrugging his shoulders.

"The weather's changing."

They stopped at the curb of the intersection and waited for the red turn signal to switch to green. Neither one of them said a word while they waited. Dawn cut her eye at Dave and saw that he was still smiling. She wondered what he was thinking about and why in the hell was he so happy. Moments later, the light turned green. Dave took a step forward and was blindsided, but not by a car. His whiplash was caused be Dawn's utterance of four words.

"I had an abortion."

Dave turned slowly towards Dawn. She tried to read his face. His mouth was agape. His wide eyes were a vision

FRIENDS

of shock, sadness, or maybe hatred. Dawn couldn't tell, she would only assume. She remained silent, awaiting a verbal response from the man who looked like he had been tossed under a bus.

The light at the intersection had once again turned red. Pedestrians stopped, surrounding the couple. Dave didn't notice. He was still cocooned in a bubble of shock.

"Dave...David?"

"You were pregnant and didn't tell me!" Dave yelled.

The crowd drew their eyes to an embarrassed Dawn. She wanted to blink her eyes and wake up in the comfort of her own bed. Although she blinked her eyes, she was still on the corner, and the inquiring faces around her wanted answers. She grabbed Dave by his arm and pulled him away from the crowd.

"I was thinking about our careers...so yesterday I had an abortion."

"Yesterday!"

"Yes. Please, don't cause a scene!"

"You was pregnant, got an abortion without my consent, and you tell me don't cause a scene!"

"We both have promising careers ahead of us. You always speak about us becoming a power couple. I want that, too."

"What does that have to do with you not discussing my parental rights with me?"

"I was scared."

"Scared is when someone has a loaded gun to your head."

"Come on."

Dave stared at Dawn with a look of disgust, distrust, dismay, and a shitload of "Dis-" words.

"I'm done," Dave said as he wiped his palms together.

"No!"

Dave walked away, leaving Dawn standing in disbelief. When she shook off the shock of his words, she caught up with him and had to almost jog to keep up with his stride.

"Dave, I'm sorry...I panicked...I didn't think...I'm an idiot."

Dave stopped abruptly and said, "Was it my baby?"

"What?"

"Was the child mine?"

"You dirty bastard!"

Dave didn't flinch from the insult. He just looked at Dawn snobbishly, as if to say, "I'm waiting for an answer."

"Of course it was your baby?"

"Are you sure?"

"I hate you! I am faithful to you! I am not a whore!"

"My first baby," Dave said while choking back tears.

"I'm sorry."

"I can't be with you. I won't get past this."

"We can. We can. I love you."

"If you loved me, you would have talked to me first. I'm done."

"No! We're not done!"

Dawn hit Dave with a barrage of weak punches on his chest.

"This isn't over!"

"What? Are you going to kill me, like you killed My--"

Before Dave finished the obvious statement, Dawn's regret turned to anger. She slapped Dave hard across his face. The cool temperature gave the slap more of a stinging effect. Dawn stood her ground, waiting for a reaction.

Dave wanted to strike back, but he refrained. This didn't sit well with Dawn, who wanted a physical confrontation. She was yearning for a fight. Maybe it was her subconscious suggesting that she needed her ass whipped for her misdeed. Whatever the case, Dawn clenched her tiny fist and swung, grazing Dave's chin.

"This is what you do! Use violence to solve your problems!"

FRIENDS

Dave's sarcasm and lack of pain from the punch moved Dawn to tears of anger as she swung wildly at him. He had to suffer getting hit before he was able to arrest her wrists. He began shaking her in an effort to kill her fight so that she could calm down. Out of nowhere, two uniformed police officers tackled Dave to the ground. One cop wedged his knee in the small of Dave's back while the other cop twisted Dave's arms back to slap on the handcuffs.

"Stop resisting!" the officer said.

"Get off me!"

"Get off of him! It's a misunderstanding!"

After flashing her credentials, Dawn employed her legal jargon to explain that she and Dave were lawyers and were not fighting, but having a dispute about a criminal case. The cops were persuaded enough to remove the cuffs from Dave's wrists. Dave brushed off his clothes, glared at Dawn, and then briskly walked away.

In a nearby bathroom, Dawn kneeled to the floor, sobbing in her hands.

• • •

Tracy stormed out of Anthony's office, slamming the door behind her. She wanted to kick herself for going back there. Even before entering his office, she knew in her heart that it would be fruitless trying to convince him to reconsider her termination, but she had to try.

Now she sat agitatedly behind the wheel of her parked car, massaging her temples while contemplating her next move. With nothing else on her agenda, she decided to go back home.

Twenty minutes later, she walked through her front door to a quiet house. Immediately, she picked up her cell phone to call Joann and inquire about her and Tammy's whereabouts. Before Tracy could punch in the number, she spotted Joann's jacket lying across the chair. Tracy sat the phone down, assuming the girls were upstairs in Tammy's room probably asleep or watching television.

Tracy kicked off her shoes, lay down on the sofa, and called Sam, informing her about the meeting with Anthony. Fed up with twenty minutes of listening to what she should've done to Anthony, Tracy said her goodbyes and rushed upstairs to the bathroom to pee.

After doing her business, she exited the bathroom and took a step towards Tammy's room, but she paused when she thought she heard a sound coming from her own room.

She walked curiously over to her closed bedroom door, turned her ear to the door, and waited. Just as she expected, she heard a female moan.

"I know this bitch don't have somebody in my damn room!"

Like a one-woman DEA Agent on a drug raid, Tracy burst into the room. Joann, who was straddling a man lying on the bed, froze in fear. Joann looked back over her shoulder at Tracy with terror in her eyes.

"What the fuck is this!" Tracy said.

"It's Tracy!" Joann screamed as she leapt to her feet.

Slowly, the man lying on the bed rose. With his face saturated with sweat and eyes replete with shame, Rob looked up at Tracy and lowered his head disgracefully in his hands. For a short moment, Tracy's body, mind, and emotions became immobilized from disbelief.

"Rob," she said questioningly, as if she was assuring herself that her eyes hadn't deceived her.

"Baby...I'm so sorry," Rob said.

In a sudden rage, Tracy charged Joann, wrestling her to the floor by her hair. In the midst of whaling away on Joann, Tracy noticed a small rip in the strap of the negligee Joann was wearing. It was a tear Tracy inadvertently had caused two weeks earlier.

"You have on my shit!"

With her fury increased, Tracy resumed her assault upon Joann, whose face was besmirched with blood. By now, Rob had slipped on his pants. Though it was difficult, he pulled a kicking and screaming Tracy away from her victim.

"Let me the fuck go!"

"Calm down!"

"He doesn't love you! With your old ass pussy!" Joann yelled before darting out the door.

"Let me go! I'm going to kill this bitch!"

With much effort, Tracy wiggled free of Rob's grasp, but before she could reach the door to pursue Joann, Rob grabbed her from behind, lifting her off her feet.

"Tracy, I'm sorry."

"Fuck you! Put me down!"

"We need to talk!"

"We didn't need to talk last night! Put me down!"

Rob lowered Tracy to her feet. She turned around cursing and punching on his chest until she tired out. He pulled her close in his arms; she placed her head on his chest, spilling tears of another heartbreak in life. Seconds later, she pushed him away.

"How could you hurt me?"

"I'm sorry."

"How could you hurt meeeee?"

"Baby, I feel like dying for what I've done. This fucking country is so fucked up. You have the president with all these damn lies. It's kids in Africa starving!"

Tracy shook her head confusingly at Rob and said, "What the fuck are you talking about?"

"It's so much shit going on!"

"Motherfucker, get out of my house!"

"You have to understand me?"

"Get the hell out!"

Rob shot a look at the door. Tracy spun around in that direction thinking Joann had returned. It was Tammy standing in the doorway with tears in her eyes.

"Tammy, go back to your room."

Tammy didn't move.

"Please leave my house, Rob," Tracy said in an even voice.

Before Rob could respond, Tracy picked Tammy up and carried her back to her own bedroom. Tracy sat in a chair cradling Tammy in her arms, reassuring the child that everything was okay. After Tammy settled down, Tracy laid her on the bed and told Tammy she will be right back.

Tracy walked back to her bedroom and was pleased – but also crushed to see that Rob had left as she had ordered. With her shattered heart strewn across the floor like autumn leaves on the forest ground, Tracy lay on the floor in a fetal position and sobbed.

. . .

A'Man parked his car in the parking spot down the street from his house. He walked back towards a car pulling into the spot behind him. When the car had parked, A'Man opened the door and extended his hand inside the car to his female companion behind the wheel. The woman who emerged from the car was Robin, Sam's acquaintance from the supermarket.

Ten minutes earlier in the supermarket parking lot, A'Man ran into Robin, whose car was parked next to his.

"You're Sam's friend, right?" Robin asked offhandedly.

"I wouldn't call us friends."

Thereafter, a flirtatious conversation commenced that was laced with an overdose of flattery, compliments, and a touch of her hair by A'Man. When A'Man asked Robin to follow him a couple blocks over to his place for a friendly drink and causal conversation, Robin hesitated a moment, then thought *what the fuck*.

A'Man took Robin's hand in his own as they walked to his house. She could have died from the fear that someone might see them. Nevertheless, she didn't free her hand. When they reached their destination, they stopped, horrified and shocked to see a dead rat at the floor of A'Man's front door.

"That damn bitch!"

"You know who did this?"

"My fucking wife!"

FRIENDS

The incident shocked Robin back to her senses. Realizing that she was about to commit adultery on the strength of flattery and compliments from a seasoned player, Robin felt less than the dead rat.

"I have to go."

"Don't go."

"I have to."

"Why? It's cool. My wife and I are going through a divorce and she keeps doing this type of shit."

"No, I really need to go", Robin said, walking back to her car.

A'Man watched disappointedly as Robin drove away. He then turned his attention to the rat, wondering if his crazy wife had killed the rodent herself or found the carcass in an alley or abandoned lot.

"Shit, He said as he threw his hands up in exasperation.

. . .

Tracy pulled herself up from her bedroom floor, dried her eyes with her shirt sleeve, then she walked in front of the mirror and stared at her miserable reflection. Like any woman who had experienced the trauma of walking in on her boyfriend and a family member having sex, Tracy questioned: was she pretty enough? Did she fall in love too soon, or perhaps, the old saying was indeed true that 90% of men were dogs. Several more questions of this nature would travel through her mind while she moved closer to the mirror, analyzing and overly amplifying every little blemish on her pretty face.

Eventually, she tore herself away from the mirror. First order of business was to check on Tammy, who was in her bedroom asleep. The second order of business was a trip to the kitchen where she grabbed a large, plastic trash bag along with a pair of latex gloves that she put on as she headed back to her bedroom.

With disgust etched across her face, Tracy snatched the tainted sheets from the bed, stuffing them in the trash bag. She contemplated taking the mattress out to a lot and burning it, but she couldn't afford to purchase a new one, so the mattress was given a reprieve.

Placing her hands on her waist, she scanned the bedroom for any property of Rob's that he may have left behind. Although her mind wrestled with moments of despondency caused by the earlier drama, Tracy had the wits to know that after a mate or spouse is kicked out of the house, they would sometimes intentionally leave something behind as a reason to return, using the opportunity to beg for a second chance.

And sure enough, on the floor by the bed was Rob's watch. She picked up the watch while assessing the value--thirty or forty dollars tops—then she dropped it in the trash bag. She was satisfied that every residue of Rob was in the trash bag or had been taken by him. Tracy picked up the bag ready to leave, yet, she didn't move. Out of the corner of her eye she saw her panty drawer ajar.

A picture of Joann wearing her negligee flashed in Tracy's mind. Tracy shooed away the vision, but the vision returned like a boomerang.

Tracy hated what she had to do next. But it had to be done, because every time she put on her panties and bras, she knew that she would never be able to shake the thought that Joann probably had them on her ass. So one by one, Tracy tossed her panties and bras in the trash bag.

As Tracy slowly disposed of the undergarments, she remembered the money she had stashed in the dresser. She frantically snatched opened the bottom drawer, reached underneath a pair of jeans, and with relief, she smiled until she opened the envelope and found only a hundred dollars. There had been seven hundred dollars in there previously. Tracy panicked. The money was her entire savings.

"Joann!"

Tracy dashed out of the room, down the stairs, grabbed her car keys, and was out of the door when she suddenly remembered Tammy. For a moment, she mindlessly considered leaving the child home alone, but common sense prevailed.

As Tracy sped through traffic, she glanced in her rearview mirror at Tammy, whose eyes were wide with fear. Tracy eased her foot off of the gas pedal. Nevertheless, she arrived at Joann's house in record time. Joann lived with her mother Rose, who was Tracy's aunt.

Pulling Tammy like a rag doll, Tracy raced into Joann's house without knocking. Joann's mother and Tracy's mother were sitting in the living room talking and were startled by Tracy's unexpected entrance.

"Where is Joann?"

"Where are your manners?" Tracy's mother said.

"She's not here," Rose said.

"She stole my fucking money!"

"Watch your mouth!" Tracy's mother snapped.

"Joann wouldn't steal from you," Rose said.

"Why do you have that baby out here in her pajamas?" Tracy's mother asked.

"When was the last time you seen Joann?" Tracy directed to Rose while ignoring her mother.

"Well, she left this morning --"

Before Rose could finish, Tracy ran upstairs to Joann's bedroom. Tracy searched the room, finding nothing but a pair of her jeans that she had loaned to Joann a year ago. She was about to take the pants, but she remembered that she didn't want to wear anything Joann had had her ass in.

Tracy returned to the living room frustrated. "Come on Tammy," Tracy said without looking in her mother's direction.

"Why do you think Joann stole your money?" Rose asked.

"If she would sleep with my man, she would steal my money."

"You're always accusing someone of doing something to hurt you," Tracy's mother said.

"You don't know shit!"

"I think you should wait here until Joann comes home?" Rose suggested.

"No. I have to make another stop."

"You're dragging that girl around the streets in bed clothes," The mother said.

"Aunt Rose, can you watch Tammy for me?"

Rose paused, "Uh, how long?"

"Not long."

"Alright, don't be long."

"Mom, I know it was you that gave Steve my address."

"He's her father."

"Next time, mind your business."

Before Tracy's mother could respond to her sarcasm, Tracy was out the door, in her car, and speeding to Rob's place. Five minutes later, Tracy banged on Rob's front door, rang his bell nonstop, and screamed for him to open the door. A neighbor peeked out her window to see what the ruckus was about.

"Open this damn door!"

Finally, Rob stuck his head out of the second floor window yelling, "I don't have time for this shit. You told me to leave your house and I did. What do you want?"

"I know that bitch is here. She stole my money."

"I don't know what you're talking about."

"Tell Joann to come to the door!"

"She's not here!"

Rob lied. Joann was standing behind him, listening.

"I know she's here. I just want my money."

"She's not here. Go home."

"Tell that bitch to come here. I'm not playing, Rob."

Tracy turned her back to the door and began kicking it like a mule. While Rob and Tracy screamed back and forth at each other, Joann called the police.

"Rob, if you don't send that bitch out here, I'm going to bust out your car windows."

"Tracy don't --"

Two minutes later, Tracy followed up on her threat by hurling a brick at Rob's car windshield. Fortunately for the windshield, it survived with just a tiny crack.

"Get the hell out here Joann!" Tracy said.

Unsatisfied with the lack of damage to the windshield, Tracy retrieved the brick. This time she was determined to put more effort in her throw. She raised the brick slightly above her head. However, before she could hurl the brick, Rob arrested her wrist. The brick fell to the ground.

"You're going to pay for that!" Rob yelled, pointing at the windshield.

"She stole my money!"

"I don't know what you're talking about. Plus, I don't have anything to do with that if she did."

"She stole six hundred dollars from my dresser drawer. That money was for my bills."

"Listen, she's not here --"

"Ain't nobody steal your money!" Joann said as she stood in the doorway.

"I thought she wasn't here?" Tracy said to Rob. "Bitch, I know you got my money. I'm not playing."

Tracy headed towards Joann. But Rob blocked the way by standing in front of Tracy.

"Move!"

"You can't come around here with this drama."

"You're good. A professional liar. And Tammy really liked you."

Rob looked disappointedly at Tracy, who stared back at him until he lowered his eyes shamefully.

"I'll give you the money out of my pocket."

"Give it here. It's six hundred."

"I don't have it right now, but you'll have it in a couple of days."

"I don't believe shit you say. I thought you had some class. You fucked that nasty bitch. A dirty bitch that would stick her ass in another woman's panties."

Rob placed his hand over his face, surprised and disturbed by the allegation. Tracy used the opportunity to maneuver past him. In the span of one hour, Joann was suffering a second beating at the hands of Tracy. Once again, Rob came to the rescue, and again he wasn't quick enough to prevent Tracy from busting Joann's nose. Tracy looked pleased to see the injuries she inflicted upon her cousin.

"I'm going to get you!" Joann screamed.

"Get my money!"

During the argument between the two women--with Rob in the center refereeing—the police arrived. Joann rushed over to them, screaming that she had been assaulted by Tracy. From Joann's bloody face, along with the neighbor's account of the incident, Tracy was arrested and placed in the back seat of a patrol car. A tear fell from her eye as she was driven away, to the delight of Joann.

After being fingerprinted and booked on charges of aggravated assault, disturbing the peace, and property damage, Tracy was placed in a holding cell. This was Tracy's first time she had stepped foot in a police station.

Tracy sat on a wooden bench terrified. She was alone in the holding cell and too overwhelmed to wipe the tears spilling down her face. The police had treated her harshly, ignoring her complaints that she was the true victim. She was explaining to deaf ears that her money had been stolen by Joann.

Suddenly, the door to the holding cell opened. Tracy leapt to her feet, hoping that it was the officer there to inform her that it was all a big misunderstanding. Tracy's hope died instantly when two women entered and the door locked behind them. Tracy sat quietly on the bench while the two women moved to the far end of the holding cell, chatting casually as if they had been through this before.

Occasionally, the women would glance over at Tracy. Although their looks or gestures weren't threatening, Tracy wished she was invisible, better yet, somewhere else.

As the minutes snailed along, somehow a conversation was struck up between Tracy and the two women. Tracy told them about her situation, beginning with walking in on Rob and Joann. Tracy was right in her assessment of the women. They were, in fact, veterans of the penal and judicial system.

They explained to Tracy that her case was bullshit and she would more than likely be released on R.O.R. (released on her recognizance), which meant in short: Tracy would not have to pay a bond to get out, but she would still be required to appear in court. They even offered to kick Joann's ass when they got out themselves. Tracy told them she might take them up on their offer.

The women's advice and information seemed to settle Tracy's emotions. Her thoughts moved to the night she met Rob at the club. Her instinct told her that he was trouble, but Dawn insisted that she talk to Rob.

Dawn's words from the night at the club echoed in Tracy's mind, "Rob is the coolest guy in the world. He knows how to treat a woman. Trust me, I'm your friend."

The door to the holding cell opened. The officer pointed at Tracy, asking her if she wanted to use the phone. Tracy almost slipped as she rushed to the door.

When she picked up the phone, she debated whom she should call, Dawn or Sam. She chose Dawn based on her occupation. Several hours later, the two women's information proved correct. Tracy was released on R.O.R.

She exited the police station with a half-hearted smile as the cool night air kissed her face, dusting off the indignity of having had her liberty stripped for what seemed like days.

Tracy folded her arms across her chest and looked up and down the block. Minutes later, Sam's car pulled up, to Tracy's surprise. Tracy spoke to the children in the back seat as she climbed in the passenger's seat.

"What happened to Dawn?"

"She called me after you called her. Gave me some bull-crap. This is what I mean. You get fired for helping her out and when you need her, where is she at?"

"It's okay, you're here."

"What happened?"

Tracy glanced back at the kids, "I'm tired. I just want to pick up Tammy and go home and get in my bed. I'll tell you everything tomorrow."

Tracy picked Tammy up from Joann's house without incident, save the complaining from Rose for having to watch Tammy for eight hours.

...

In a quiet upscale apartment complex, Dawn paced the hallway outside of Dave's apartment, waiting to surprise him when he came home. She had been wearing out the carpet for twenty minutes. As the minutes turned into an hour, Dawn wondered if she should just leave and try to catch him tomorrow. But her heart kept her there. Reverberating in her mind was the notion that her future was at stake.

To help her cause with the kiss-and-makeup attempt, Dawn brought along an expensive bottle of wine and an epicurean dinner in a heated container. The icing on the cake would come in the form of a foolproof apology.

Earlier that day at the law firm, Dawn sat at her desk writing, rewriting, and rehearsing her apology speech. Just when she was about to add the finishing touches, she received a call from a frantic Tracy, screaming that she had been arrested and needed help.

Immediately, Dawn went into lawyer mode. She advised Tracy not to say a word to the police if she hadn't made a statement already. Tracy assured Dawn that she had said nothing. Dawn told Tracy to sit tight and she would be there promptly to bail her out.

After Dawn hung up the phone, she sighed heavily. Tracy's arrest had thrown a monkey wrench in Dawn's plans for the night. Dawn thought for a moment, pondering her dilemma: should she abandon her plans to serenade Dave or bail out her friend?

The way Dawn saw it, Tracy shouldn't have been fighting in the streets over a man, and the charges weren't all that serious. So Dawn figured she would compromise. She called Sam, explaining that she was held up at the firm with the partners working on a capital murder case and would be tied up for hours, and it would be up to Sam to bail out Tracy.

After hanging up from Sam, Dawn resumed the finishing touches on her apology. Satisfied with her work, she hurried out the office and headed out to Dave's. During her drive, not once did Dawn bat an eye at abandoning her friend.

The main door to the apartment complex opened and Dawn perked up with anticipation—the moment had arrived, or so she thought. It was an old woman and her small dog returning home from their nightly walk.

Dawn glanced impatiently at her watch. A half- hour later, with Dave still a no-show, the first sense of guilt penetrated her selfish heart for not giving the necessary aid to Tracy. To vanquish her guilt, Dawn told herself, *you first.*

Becoming tired from pacing, Dawn sat on the floor with her back leaning against Dave's door. She glanced at the bottle of wine next to her and considered taking a drink when her cell phone rang.

"Hello?"

"Hey, young lady," Mr. Hall said calmly.

Dawn was ready to make an excuse to get off of the phone but decided to use the call with her "secret friend" to kill time while she ironically waited for the man she loved.

"And how are you?" Dawn asked.

"I'm well. How is your friend? You rushed out of here today like it was a fire."

"She's doing better."

"What are you doing?"

"Nothing, just sitting around."

"Can you talk?"

"Yes."

Later, Dawn would wish she had said, *no, it's not a good time to talk.*

"When are we going to get together? You know I hate it when I go a week without touching your soft skin and smelling your hair," Mr. Hall asked.

"You touched my shoulders today at the office, and I believe you smelled my hair while you stood behind me."

"Cute and clever," said Mr. Hall with a light chuckle. "Again, when are we going to get together?"

As soon as I stop bleeding from this abortion, Dawn wanted to say, but she settled for, "Soon."

"What are you wearing?"

"The clothes I was wearing earlier."

"Well, you want to know what I'm wearing."

No, I do not.

"Absolutely nothing. I'm lying across the bed naked as the day I came into the world."

Duh, Dawn thought. There was a pause in the conversation. She could hear Mr. Hall shifting on the bed.

"Where is your wife?"

"If you really want to know, she's away from the house... maybe she's out with her boyfriend," said Mr. Hall with a chuckle.

"Your wife has a boyfriend?"

"I don't know... I have a girlfriend, so the possibility exists of her engaging in infidelity also. Do you agree?"

Dawn didn't answer. She didn't like the idea of being called a "girlfriend." She considered her relationship with Mr. Hall more of an agreement than a commitment.

"Are you there?" Mr. Hall asked.

"Yes. I was just imagining a sixty-year- old Mrs. Hall spending the evening with a thirty-year-old African-American stud."

"It would serve me right for being with a thirty-year -old African- American myself... What are you doing here? Are you trying to make me jealous?"

"No, I was merely pointing out what's good for the goose is good for the gander."

"Forget that nonsense. I wish we could get together for at least an hour or so. What do you say, baby?"

"That's not possible."

"Well, at least talk to me baby."

"I am talking."

"You know... talk to me."

"I have to go take care of something -"

"You would crumble under cross-examination. You just told me earlier in the conversation that you're just sitting around. Now you contradict yourself baby... Talk to me."

Dawn looked up at the ceiling and imitated hitting herself repeatedly on the head with her phone.

"I'm waiting. I need to hear your sweet, sexy voice darling."

Dawn cleared her throat away from the phone. In a low voice just above a whisper, she said, "Picture me naked...lying next to your warm body. Picture my honey-colored skin; your warm gentle hands are fondling my breast while you nibble on my ear. Are your eyes closed, daddy?"

"Yes, they are beautiful."

"You pour honey on my breast, you circle my nipples with your tongue, then suck on them. How do they taste, daddy?" Dawn said as she shook her head.

"They taste like honey."

"Picture the two of us in your office. We just won a case and the reward is millions. It's time to celebrate. You approach me from behind and pull my skirt down to my ankles. I lean over your desk on a stack of important legal papers, you do me hard from behind... your wife enters, but we do not stop, in fact, you go harder."

"Yeah, fuck her baby."

"We're alone in a hotel room. You crawl between my legs, kissing and licking my thighs. You lick my clit like a kitten licking up milk from a bowl...you taste my cum. You bite my ass softly. I wrap my hand around your erection, I'm stroking you hard, harder and faster."

Dawn could hear Mr. Hall breathing heavily. She figured he was jerking off.

"Go, daddy, go... you're fucking me everywhere, hard, real hard, you're trying to kill me. You're deep inside of me," Dawn said, thinking, *yeah right.*

"Uhhh," Mr. Hall moaned. "Baby, you're terrific, young and vibrant. I can't wait until we get together. Listen, you have a good night."

"Sleep well."

Dawn hung up the cell phone and closed her eyes for a moment to wind down. She stood slowly, hoping the dirtiness she felt blanketing her would fall to the floor.

The enthusiasm and confidence she had of persuading Dave to forgive had faded. She picked up the food and wine, placed the bottle underneath her arm, kissed her open hand, and placed her kissed hand upon Dave's door, then she walked out into the night.

CHAPTER

3

"They were right here," said Tracy, pointing at her bed. "I'm still sick about it. The nerve of that whore to squeeze her nasty ass into my panties. And Rob is just as trifling for sticking his dick in that grimy bitch."

Sam was unusually silent, trapped in her own thoughts. She wondered how she would've responded if it was she who discovered Andrew in bed with another woman. Surprisingly, the idea of Andrew's infidelity didn't disturb her a least bit. In fact, from her viewpoint, it would be a welcoming excuse to divorce him. While Sam's mind wandered in wishful thinking and hopeful possibilities, Tracy stared at her questionably.

"What's on your mind, Sammy?"

"I was just thinking about your case. How could your own cousin put you in this situation? I used to like Joann... She wasn't even thinking about what could happen to Tammy."

"I will never be separated from my daughter," said Tracy confidently. "Somebody told me that all I have to do is get Joann not to come to the preliminary hearing and the case will be dropped."

"A lawyer told you that?"

"Two women in the holding cell."

"Jailhouse lawyers."

"They were right about me signing for my own bail... I'm going to run it by Dawn and get her opinion."

Sam rolled her eyes, making certain that Tracy saw her displeasure with getting Dawn involved.

"What?" Tracy asked, holding her hands out.

"Dawn doesn't know shit."

"She knows enough to become a lawyer."

"She's a fucking rookie."

"Rookie or veteran, she's still a lawyer, and I don't have the money to hire one."

"They will give you a public defender to represent you. I'm not a lawyer, but I know that," Sam said with sarcasm.

"What would it hurt to get free and straight-up legal advice from a friend?"

"That bitch ain't never been straight-up."

"Please, not right now! Just because y'all had another squabble, I'm not supposed to get her help?"

"You do what's best for you. But when she fucks your case up, don't come crying to me, because I'm going to say I told you so."

"I don't understand y'all. One day y'all sisters, and the next day you two are enemies. It doesn't make sense. It's like there's some sort of underlying resentment going on."

"If there is, it's not me. She's the one who's quick to compare her life to others'. Always talking about what she is and what she's got. You just don't be paying attention...I have no problem putting her in her place."

"But she's not here right now, and you're talking about her. I'm not trying to hear it."

"You're right."

Five minutes later, Dawn entered the bedroom melodramatically. She rushed over to Tracy, hugging her tightly.

"Are you okay, honey? I know sitting in that funky holding cell was a nightmare."

"I'm alright," Tracy said. She looked over Dawn's shoulder at Sam.

Sam snickered as she stared at Dawn's back, wishing her stare was a dagger.

Dawn released Tracy, walked over to the bed, and placed her hands on her hips, "I hope this is a new mattress."

"I threw away the sheets. I can't afford to just go out and buy a new mattress."

"I'm going to curse Rob's ass out," Dawn said.

Sam tried to remain silent, but she couldn't resist the urge to comment. "I thought Rob was all that?" Sam said deridingly.

Dawn looked annoyed but attached a smile to her agitation as she walked over to Sam, who stood poised for an altercation.

"I don't want to fight with you. I'm going through my own breakup," Dawn said unaggressively.

"You told Dave about the abortion?" Tracy asked.

"Yes, it was awful. We were heading to lunch when I told him. Our business was overheard by a large crowd. The police got involved."

"Whatever. Right now it's about Tracy. She's the one with major problems. She might be going to jail."

Dawn was on the brink of firing back at Sam until she saw the pain in Tracy's tired eyes.

"You're right Sam. It's about Tracy. I'm glad I'm afforded the opportunity to give a friend my legal expertise."

Sam gave Tracy the I-told-you-so look.

"Tell me everything that happened, and don't leave out a single fact, no matter how insignificant it may appear to be."

Tracy revealed every detail: from walking in on the cheaters to signing the R.O.R. papers. To Tracy's delight, Dawn confirmed the information that the two women from the holding cell had conveyed to her. The case would be thrown out if Joann didn't show up in court.

"The simple question is how do we get Joann not to come to court?" Sam interjected.

"I can kill her. Surely she deserves it," Tracy said.

"You're not murdering anyone, although, she does deserves it," Dawn said.

"Maybe you can speak with her mother to talk some sense into her," Sam said.

"What if she wants money?" Dawn asked.

"She already stole my money...Dawn, that's one of the reasons I asked you to come over...I need some help."

Dawn hesitated, "I'm scheduled to put a substantial amount of money on my new home next week, but I'll see what I can do."

Sam gave Tracy a look that was intercepted by Dawn.

"I'm going to do what I can." Dawn directed her words to Sam.

"Shit, you should be glad to help her out. You hooked her up with the dude. She didn't even want to get with him. But you said he's cool, he's this, and he's that."

Dawn was on fire. Sam could see the imaginary flames blazing in Dawn's eyes. But Sam didn't care. She continued quoting Dawn on how terrific a guy Rob was.

"I'm not going to feed," Dawn said calmly, regaining her composure.

"This is all your fault," said Sam.

Dawn looked offended, "How is this my fault?"

"You wanted Tracy to get with the guy, for whatever reason, it had to be somehow to your benefit."

"You're crazy," Dawn said with a laugh.

"Fuck you, Dawn. You me-first bitch!"

"Fuck you."

Before Tracy could interpose, Sam responded by grabbing Dawn's neck in an open-handed chocked grip. Both Dawn and Tracy were shocked by Sam's physical aggression. In past years, many of the arguments that had transpired between the friends never raised to this level of violence.

"Get off of her."

Tracy snatched Sam away from Dawn.

"If I didn't have that procedure yesterday--" Dawn warned.

Sam remained quiet, realizing the magnitude of her actions, but pride prevented an apology.

"What the hell is wrong with you?" Tracy yelled.

"I don't know," Sam said.

"You need to find out!" Dawn yelled as she rubbed her sore neck.

Without looking at Dawn or Tracy, Sam picked up her pocketbook and immediately left the room, leaving the girls even more in shock than they were by Sam's physical action toward Dawn.

"I'm going to ask my uncle what's going on with her."

"No, we just all need to sit down and talk."

After Dawn agreed to give Tracy a loan, she left. Tracy lay sprawled across the bed, shaking her head pessimistically about her future.

...

A'Man walked out of the police station feeling like a pussy. That's precisely how three uniformed police officers made him feel when they whispered and snickered among themselves upon hearing him inform the duty sergeant that he wanted to get a restraining order against his estranged wife.

Although the trip to the police station had rendered A'Man the butt of jokes, it wasn't solely an embarrassment, thanks to the cute female detective clad in a pinstripe pantsuit. She handed A'Man the card of a lawyer who was excellent in divorce cases. Never missing the opportunity to engage a hottie, A'Man struck up a conversation that ended with the detective writing her cell phone number on the back of the card.

A'Man pocketed the card and grinned sinisterly at the prospect of Mirrar paying him spousal support, or better yet, him winning a decree and being entitled to half her money. The only reason A'Man married Mirrar in the first place was because of her money. But after discovering that she was a beautiful lunatic, it was time for him to go.

Later that afternoon, A'Man entered the law firm of Hall & Johnson and Associates. After a twenty minute meeting with Mr. Hall, A'Man felt confident that he would be granted some portion of Mirrar's money if he followed the lawyer's instructions.

While waiting for the elevator, A'Man encountered Dawn. She, too, was waiting for the elevator along with a male paralegal. Uninterested was A'Man's initial reaction to Dawn. Who checked him over with a glance. But when A'Man overhead the paralegal mention to Dawn that he was going to copy her brief, inferring that she was a lawyer, A'Man changed his stance.

He flirted with his eyes and flashed the award-winning smile. When the paralegal left their presence, A'Man made his move. He began by complementing Dawn on her clothing.

He looks good, Dawn thought as she gave him a coy smile.

It was the kind of smile that A'Man was very familiar with. But to his surprise, Dawn rejected him politely when he turned up the charm.

After A'Man had left the building, Dawn learned that he had just retained Mr. Hall to represent him in a divorce case. Dawn wiped her brow at the thought of the close call. Not only would it have been unethical to date a client, she would also have to contend with Mr. Hall's jealousy and the reprisal from it.

Dawn entered her office, flattered by the interest A'Man had shown towards her. Adulation coming from someone sexy for a change ignited a spark that shot through her body.

As she eased down to sit in front of her computer, she imagined herself naked, sitting on A'Man's lap. She giggled at the erotic thought that was contrary to her favorite position: laying face down with a pillow underneath her lower torso to elevate her ass in the air. With a mountain of research in front of her, she put A'Man and kinky sex out of her mind, turned on the computer, and got down to business.

As her fingers flew over the keyboard, the incident that occurred between her and Sam at Tracy's house crossed her mind, disrupting her typing. Unable to focus on the task at hand, Dawn leaned back in her chair trying to recall what she could've possibly said to trigger a physical reaction from Sam.

While she mulled over each of her responses to Sam's sarcasm, nothing particularly harsh stood out. Then like a backhand slap to the mouth, it hit her. It was the statement that Sam had made.

Although Dawn was unable to recount Sam's words verbatim, she remembered something to the effect that hooking Rob and Tracy up was somehow to her own benefit. *That's preposterous!* Dawn thought noting that the only thing she got out of the failed relationship was a headache and a sore neck. Dawn picked up the phone to question Andrew about Sam's recent behavior, but she put the phone down, recalling Tracy's advice for her not to get involved.

The drama brought thoughts of Dave to mind. Dawn hoped that time had quelled his anger towards her. In spite of their breakup, Dawn still wanted to be that power couple that she and Dave envisioned for their future.

Dawn called his number and felt optimistic when he told her that he was still in love with her but needed time to get over the hurt of her betrayal. Dawn said she understood and would be there whenever Dave was ready to resume their relationship.

The call ended with Dawn telling Dave, in a sincere voice, that she loved him, too. Before she could sit back and digest her phone conversation, Mr. Hall had eased silently into her office and was at her side massaging her right shoulder with a strong hand.

"I miss you, baby," Mr. Hall whispered.

As Dawn stood to remove Mr. Hall's hand tactfully from her shoulder, she thought, *this is going to end in a mess*.

...

Tracy slammed her foot on the brake pedal, bringing the Pathfinder to a screeching stop inches away from rear-ending the truck in front of her. The truck also had to come to a sudden halt because of an accident several cars up ahead. It would be twenty minutes before the traffic on the crowded highway could resume.

Following the sudden stop, Tracy looked in the back seat, where a smiling Tammy sat safely secured, strapped into her seat belt. Sam sat in the passenger seat jolted. She had one hand firmly on the dashboard and the other hand over her thumping heart, thankful that she was wearing her seat belt.

Tracy sighed heavily as she glanced at the time on her watch. It was ten minutes to six. Rob told her to be at his house by six.

"I know if I'm late, Rob would have some excuse for why he had to leave the house. Then it would be another reason why he had to use the money he promised me. These things always seem to happen to me."

"You're not the only one," said Sam hoarsely.

While Sam vainly checked her face and hair in the sun-visor mirror, Tracy dialed Rob on her cell phone. The look of disappointment washed over her face when she got his voicemail.

"Leave a message," said Sam.

"What for"? If he's going to give me the money, I'm going to get it. If he's bullshitting, fuck it...What was up with you putting your hands on Dawn? You crossed the line."

"I know it was wrong, but I've been under a lot of stress."

"What's going on?"

"Nothing really". Probably that fight with Anthony."

"Sam, who do you think you're talking to?"

Sam began fiddling with her fingers, the classic telltale sign that something was bothering her. She badly wanted to confide in Dawn about the abuse that she was enduring day-in and day-out at the hands of Andrew. For her part, Sam had been a pro at keeping her home-life troubles hidden from her girls. Andrew added to the charade by playing the role of the good husband in front of Sam's friends.

"Sam, you can talk to me about anything."

"Andrew ain't shit!"

Even without any earlier evidence indicating that Andrew was the culprit of any marital high-crimes or misdemeanors, Sam's declaration wasn't a surprise to Tracy; she would argue vehemently to her grave that 95% of a woman's troubles were caused by a man directly or indirectly. "Does every man cheat?" Tracy declared, without looking for an answer.

"He's not cheating. At least I don't believe he is…He hits me and calls me every bitch in the book."

"Not Andrew!"

"Yes, Andrew…In public he's always on his best behavior, but at home he can be like the devil."

Sam opened the flood gates; what came next was a tide of tears, pain, and torment that had been bundled up for years. Unleashing her abuse was unburdening.

Like a good friend/therapist, Tracy listened quietly. Several times she had to hold back a tear as Sam described the physical abuse. Tracy recommended to Sam that she should tell Andrew that he should get help for his anger. Tracy also advised that if there was no effort to change on Andrew's part, Sam should leave, feeling no regrets or qualms for her decision. Sam didn't have a response to either of Tracy's suggestions.

Traffic finally started to move. Without further discussions on Sam's situation, Tracy drove quickly to Rob's house, arriving there twenty minutes after six.

When Rob didn't answer the door after several heavy knocks, and a continuous ringing of the bell, Tracy was beginning to believe that he wasn't home or avoiding to answer the door. She cursed herself for being tardy. When she turned to leave, Rob opened the door, to Tracy's relief.

He invited Tracy to come inside for a moment. She declined, offering the excuse that Sam had to get home to her children. Rob waved to Sam, who was watching the couple. She responded by rolling her eyes. Rob smiled as if he expected that kind of reaction from Sam.

"I'm sorry for everything that happened between us. I never meant for us to end like this."

"Do you have my money?"

"Yeah. But I want you to know that I didn't take your money."

When Rob handed Tracy six hundred-dollar bills, her anxiety vanished. She told Rob that she needed one more favor, which was for him to convince Joann not to come to court. After she explained that her case would be dismissed if Joann was a no-show, Rob assured Tracy that Joann wouldn't show up to court. It was the sincerity in Rob's voice that made Tracy allow him to hug her goodbye.

When Sam saw Tracy and Rob embrace, she was furious. Sam didn't know that it was a farewell embrace. She sprung from the car like Tracy was being assaulted and needed her help. Sam cursed Rob and had to be pulled away from him by Tracy.

During the drive to her house, Sam explained that she had just snapped. Tracy warned Sam that she had to get her anger in order before she seriously hurt someone, or she gets hurt.

Later that evening, Sam put her children to bed early. The children's ages ranged from four to seven years old. On this particular night, Andrew was uncommonly pleasant towards Sam. She figured this would be a good time to speak with him about their marital problems.

Each time she was ready to approach him, she would lose her nerve. Finally, it was ten minutes before he needed to leave for work when she asked him to sit across from her at the kitchen table.

"What's wrong, baby?" Andrew asked in a concerned voice.

Sam smiled warmly. This was the first time in years that he referred to her as baby. She wondered if having this conversation now was even necessary.

"Andrew, our marriage is in trouble."

Andrew studied Sam's strained eyes, only looking away to watch her folded hands shake nervously as they repeatedly tapped the table.

"I love you and the children so much. The children and you are my life," Sam said with a certifying smile.

"Just come out and say it. You're fucking somebody."

"No!"

Andrew felt relieved but held his stern face. A face that almost made a fearful Sam discontinue the conversation.

"We're always fussing and fighting. Our children have to be affected by this --"

"I was in a good mood tonight, and you wanted to fuck up my evening with this nonsense. This is why we're always arguing. You start the shit around here. You don't know what to say out of your damn mouth."

Sam listened in disbelief as Andrew placed the blame of their marital problems on her lap. After five minutes of listening to his ranting and raving, Sam had reached her boiling point. She stood abruptly and slapped her palm down hard on the table, silencing him.

"You're not going to put this shit on me! You have badgered me for years! You accused me of getting pregnant by someone else! How do you think that made me feel, huh? The verbal and physical abuse will stop!"

After saying her piece, she folded her arms across her chest and waited for Andrew to apologize for his wrongs and vindicate her of every unfounded accusation against her. Unfortunately, Andrew didn't say a word. He simply glanced at his watch and walked away from the table.

Stunned by Andrew's lack of response and his cavalier brush-off, Sam rushed around the table, grabbing Andrew by his arm and spinning him to face her.

"You don't have anything to say to me?"

"I have to go to work."

"You don't care about this marriage?"

Believing that a kinder approach might change his attitude, Sam cupped Andrew's face in her hands, rubbing it with the love of a wife desperate to break through the unsympathetic wall Andrew erected between himself and his wife.

"We have to discuss our marriage, Andrew. I want things to work. We have too much time in."

"There's nothing wrong with our marriage," Andrew said coldly.

Demoralized, Sam stared at her partner of over a decade, the father of her children, the man who vowed "for better or worse." She didn't see that individual, before her was a complete stranger. She couldn't understand how he could be in such denial.

Stevie Wonder could see them fighting in the dark. A deaf person could hear their many arguments. Something is wrong with this picture, she told herself. Her thoughts were overlapping Andrew's words, "There's nothing wrong with our marriage," that were echoing in her head.

Sam wanted to say something profound that would tug at Andrew's soul and force him to come to his senses. But keen and embellishing words and phrases evaded her as if she had stage fright.

The only thing left to do was turn and walk away, which she did defeatedly. As she headed out of the kitchen and into the living room, she could feel Andrew's presence nearing her from behind. *It wasn't clever words that were needed to touch his heart after all. It was my silence,* Sam thought.

When Andrew was a couple of feet behind her, Sam stopped with a smile and waited for his embrace and apologies. But her smile perished when she felt his shoe kick her in the butt.

"Get your ass upstairs."

The kick didn't have the force of a football punt on a warm day. In fact, it wasn't physically painful at all. However, the measure of disrespect and humiliation was unimaginable.

Andrew braced himself, expecting a raging response. But Sam couldn't move or speak. At that moment, she felt lower than whale shit. She tried to hold back the tears, but her weak dam of emotions broke. Finally, she turned slowly to face her degradation. But Andrew avoided eye contact. Without a word, he grabbed his jacket and was out the door.

As Andrew sat in his car tussling with mixed emotions, he hated what he had done to the mother of his children. But he reasoned that extreme measures were necessary to ignite enough anger in Sam to leave him, because Andrew didn't have the balls to leave her and the children.

Andrew had a motive for his deplorable actions. It was his long time girlfriend and her three-year- old son, who Andrew believed was his child. For five years, Andrew's girlfriend had pressured him to leave Sam and the children, now Andrew was having second thoughts.

Back in the house, Sam caught a glimpse of her pitiful-looking self in the mirror and did a double take. In her mind, she thought she looked five years older.

Slowly, she walked up the stairs with the resemblance of a tired old woman. She eased open the door to the children's room. They were sleeping soundly. *How could a man so evil produce such beautiful children?* She wondered as she soundlessly closed the door back.

In her own bedroom, Sam removed a 5x8 glass-framed wedding photo from the dresser. She dropped the photo to the floor and stomped out the glass with her heel. As she dug her heel deep into the smiling face of Andrew, destroying the photo, she wished it was Andrew's literal face and not the picture that was meeting her heel.

With nothing left of value to destroy, Sam had an impulse to do something crazy. She sat on the edge of the bed, struggling with her mischievous mind.

Five minutes later, after succumbing to her lower desires, Sam sat in a sports bar drowning drinks and openly flirting with a guy sitting next to her. Several times the guy tried to lure Sam out the bar, and each time he failed. But as the drinks kept coming, and the conversation moved to a more sexual nature, the guy knew Sam would surely be open for business.

As Sam selectively related to the stranger bits and pieces of her troubled marriage, she saw A'Man smiling at her from across the room.

Sam wondered how long he had been eyeing her, and for a moment, she felt embarrassed that he may have seen her flirting. So what, she told herself. She finished her drink and marched over to A'Man, leaving the guy at the bar feeling cheated.

"Why do you keep following me?" Sam asked in a tipsy splutter.

"I'm not following you. Maybe you're following me."

"Maybe I am."

Sam paused, surprised by her own statement. A'Man himself was somewhat shocked by the remark. Soon, he realized it was the alcohol that was giving Sam her feistiness.

From the lascivious look Sam stared into A'Man's eyes, there was nothing left to come between them but a five-minute drive to A'Man's house. Upon arrival, A'Man was thankful that Mirrar didn't leave a surprise at his doorsteps.

On nervous legs, Sam entered A'Man's darkened bedroom. The intoxicating effects from the alcohol she had consumed just minutes earlier dwindled to almost nonexistence. However, her anger for Andrew was still at its apex, and that was the force that drove her along.

She swallowed hard at the thought of entering the danger zone and burning the bridge behind her so there would be no turning back. Without a word or foreplay, and with a vengeful face that A'Man couldn't see, Sam nonchalantly removed her clothes. A'Man followed suit.

Sam flinched when he touched her trembling body. A'Man figured this was probably the first time she had ever cheated on her husband.

As Sam lay on her back, she moaned when A'Man entered her, appreciating his size, which was much bigger than Andrew. As their bodies moved in unison, Sam wrapped her arms and legs around A'Man and thought little of Andrew.

Without warning, A'Man pulled out of Sam and flipped her on her stomach. He smacked her ass. She liked that—something Andrew never did. Or maybe she couldn't recall at the moment if he had ever smacked her on her ass during sex.

Quickly, A'Man re-entered Sam and gave her what she needed, a good, old-fashioned fucking from behind. After several intense minutes of fucking, Sam felt his body jerk, and she quickened her own pace to meet her lover in a climactic moment.

Afterwards, as nonchalantly as Sam had undressed, without saying a word, so did she dress.

While Sam drove home, she fought hard to smother the shame of what she had done. It wasn't until she checked on the children that it came crashing home. She stepped into the bathroom, sat on the closed toilet seat and bawled.

As she sat there crying and calling herself a dirty whore, she felt the wetness of A'Man's semen and her fluids seep into her panties.

She turned on the hot shower and undressed quickly. Since this was the first time she had ever cheated, she wasn't quite sure what to do with her panties that were filled with the incriminating DNA of a man who wasn't her husband. She panicked for a moment, and then she gained control of her frail emotions and fear of Andrew walking in on her by remembering that he was at work.

With the panties in hand, Sam stepped into the shower and washed them out. After she bathed, she threw the panties in the dryer and went to bed, sobbing until she fell asleep.

Several hours later, Sam was awakened by Andrew when he climbed in bed. Sam, who was lying on her stomach, shifted to her side with her back to Andrew as he apologized repeatedly.

When he didn't get a response to his apologies, Andrew went down on Sam, believing that the act would make up for his wrongs. Although Sam's body responded to his tongue, her hatred for him was still fresh and strong, and if she thought she could escape without him murdering her, she would've asked him, *how does the handsome man I slept with a few hours ago taste?*

Across town, Tracy's mind was so uneasy—due to her mounting problems—that she couldn't sleep. She looked at the clock. It read 2:35 a.m. She reached into her dresser drawer, pulled out a bag of Cush weed, and sat on the floor with her back against the bed while she smoked in the dark.

For a split second, she wondered if Rob and Joann were together. Even though Tracy's heart was still freshly bruised from Rob's betrayal, there remained a small part of her that somehow desired him in her life. *Why should I have to give him up to her?* Tracy foolishly asked herself.

She called to mind his kindness and generosity, weighing it against his betrayal. As the weed settled her unsteady nerves and fogged her judgment, the scale was beginning to tilt in Rob's favor.

When she was finished smoking, Tracy felt nice as she giggled while thinking, *that's just what the doctor ordered.* In the spur of the moment, Tracy picked up the phone and called Rob. He answered after six rings. Tracy hesitated; just when she found a voice to speak, she heard Joann's voice in the background.

Tracy hung up the phone feeling stupid. She knew for certain that Rob saw her number on his phone. She prayed he wouldn't call back, and he didn't.

Although Tracy wished she had never made the call, it was, after all, beneficial. Tracy didn't realize it at the time, but hearing Joann's voice erased the fingerprint that Rob had left on her heart.

With renewed stress from the phone call incident, Tracy retrieved the bag of Cush and began smoking again. This time the weed made her depressed and paranoid. No matter how hard she tried to avoid thinking about the criminal case, she couldn't shake off the possibility that she could end up doing some time. The chance of incarceration meant that Tammy could be taken away from her.

The idea of Tammy in foster care, or worse, was too inconceivable. Tracy got up, extinguished the weed, and stood in the center of the room looking for something to do to distract her mind.

Tracy removed the classified section from the newspaper and started circling possible job opportunities. Fifteen minutes later, the effects of the weed and a fragile mental state took its toll. Tracy fell asleep on the bed with the classified section lying across her chest.

...

Under the cover of darkness, the private investigator hired by Mirrar slouched down in the passenger seat of his car that was parked down the street from A'Man's house. He had been waiting patiently for hours for another shot at his targets.

A little before midnight, the P.I. arrived on the scene a moment too late, just catching a glimpse of A'Man and his female escort as they entered the house. The P.I. knew that what went in must come out. The P.I. only hoped their behavior would provide the shot he needed to close the case.

He had been trailing A'Man for a week with nothing to show but a couple of photos of A'Man and an unidentified woman standing on the corner talking.

Minutes after sunrise, the door to A'Man's house opened. The P.I. raised his 35mm camera and took aim. The woman was the first to exit, looking satisfied from a night of obvious pleasure that gave her a radiant smile. The P.I. snapped her photo, *very nice choice, A'Man.*

Seconds later, A'Man appeared in the doorway wearing a robe. He, too, sported a smile. And like his companion, his photo was also taken.

As the couple stood on the steps exchanging a few words, several photos were taken of the duo. Nevertheless, the P.I. wasn't satisfied. He needed tabloid material.

Being the gentleman-like ladies man, A'Man leaned forward and kissed the woman on her mouth. The P.I. smiled as he got his money shot. Suddenly, A'Man disengaged the kiss, to the woman's surprise. With a cautious raise of his eyebrow, A'Man took a quick look up and down the street. He saw nothing.

Although he didn't hear the shutter of a camera, A'Man had an inclination that something had just occurred. His action caused the woman to take a look around also. The P.I. could read her lips as she asked A'Man what was wrong. He shook his head, smiled, and gave her another kiss.

It would be those money shots of him kissing the woman on the mouth that would cause A'Man to walk away penniless when his divorce from Mirrar was finalized.

CHAPTER
4

Since sleeping with A'Man three days ago, Sam had been sad, enveloped with guilt, and feeling worthless. Today, she awoke plagued with those same symptoms of depression. When Sam had visited her gynecologist two days ago for her routine pelvic examinations, her doctor had noticed that she was distant. When he inquired about the matter, Sam lied, blaming her condition on exhaustion.

Not ready to face the day ahead, Sam lay still in bed, staring at the ceiling as if she was fastened by a straight-jacket. To her left lay Andrew, sleeping soundly.

Since the affair, other than her visit to the doctor, Sam hadn't left the house. When she wasn't caring for the children, she was glued to the sofa, quietly watching television, a far cry from her usually rambunctious self.

Andrew had noticed the change in his wife. Even the children could sense that something was wrong. Still, no one mentioned the matter.

Interestingly enough, during Sam's days of gloom, Andrew had been surprisingly pleasant to her, reminiscent of the earlier years of their marriage. Sam attributed his kindness to his guilt for kicking her in the butt. Whatever the reason for his change, Sam welcomed the relief from his daily doses of harassment.

After ten minutes of staring at the ceiling, Sam reluctantly climbed out of bed. She checked on the sleeping children before making her way to the kitchen to prepare breakfast. While she contemplated whether to serve the children a quick cold meal or something hot, she received a call from her gynecologist.

Without the doctor stating the nature of his call, Sam figured it couldn't be anything pleasant. Sam tried to get the information from the doctor over the phone, but the doctor insisted that she come to his office.

Twenty minutes later, Sam walked into the gynecologist's office, trying to read his face as he closed the door behind her.

"Have a seat, Sam."

Sam ignored the doctor's insistence. With fear in her eyes, she stood with her arms folded across her chest.

"Sam, when I examined you a couple days ago I found redness on your cervix. I did some tests --"

"I have cancer?"

"No."

"AIDS?" Sam yelled.

Her longtime doctor placed a consoling hand on her shoulder and delivered the bad news, "You have Gonorrhea."

"Gonorrhea!" Sam uttered in disbelief.

After taking an HIV test and receiving the obligatory speech—advice, treatment for Gonorrhea, and prescription—Sam stepped out of the doctor's office so infuriated that she had forgotten where she had parked her car. Placing her hand on her hot forehead, she took a standing-eight-second count in order to calm down and gather her senses.

Sam located her car, which was right in front of her. It took a moment for Sam's shaking hand to insert the key in the ignition. While she drove with her foot heavy on the gas pedal, she couldn't stop cursing and crying. Swirling around in her mind was the thought, *which one of those lousy bastards did this to me?*

By the time Sam turned her car into the liquor store parking lot, her anger had given way to the earlier depression she had felt before receiving the bad news.

FRIENDS

"Ain't this a bitch!" Sam yelled as she recalled the doctor's instructions not to drink alcohol while she was taking the medication.

As she sat behind the wheel thinking, she rested on the belief that it was A'Man who burned her. She couldn't bring herself to believe that it was Andrew, which would mean that he was unfaithful.

Sam started the car. She was set on hunting down A'Man and doing God knows what to him. But another thought caused her to pause. She became suspicious of Andrew and his behavior. Lately, he was being nice to her. She initially assumed it was for the kick in the butt. But now she fought the urge to assume that it could be infidelity.

Suddenly, Sam's world became even more complicated. She needed to find a secluded place to think. Her cell phone rang. She glanced at Tracy's number on the phone but didn't answer.

• • •

Meanwhile, A'Man strolled into a restaurant to use the bathroom. He stood three urinals down from an elderly man. A'Man glanced at the older gentleman and was thankful that he was still young and strong. When A'Man pulled out his penis to relieve himself, he yelled from the burning sensation that came along with the urination. The elderly man gave A'Man a wink and a chuckle as he walked by.

• • •

At 11:30 a.m. the movie theater was fairly empty. The few movie-goers that were there sat spaciously apart. Sam herself sat in the second row from the front and could care less about what was playing on the screen.

She had chosen the theater for two reasons: the first purpose was to be able to cry openly in the darkness without being questioned by a caring stranger. Lastly, for some bizarre reason, she craved buttered popcorn.

While the tears moved slowly down her cheeks, Sam stared blankly at the movie. Her first thought concerning her STD brought a twinge to her heart. It was something the doctor insisted that she do immediately. He told Sam sternly that it was imperative that she inform Andrew and A'Man of their need to get tested. If it was A'Man alone, Sam could face him, but telling Andrew was a possibility Sam didn't want to make a reality.

There was something else the doctor had said that perplexed Sam. Sam, who had never been burned before, couldn't understand how men usually developed symptoms of Gonorrhea within two or three day, while it took women much longer to develop their symptoms. This medical fact presented an additional problem for Sam.

The last time she had sex was four days ago with both A'Man and Andrew—ten hours apart. So if the doctor's information was correct, whoever had burned her would've developed their symptoms by now.

Sam began nibbling on her well-manicured fingernails, trying to put her crisis in perspective. She was ninety percent certain that Andrew wasn't burning, because if he had been, she would know it. *Unless he was cheating and hiding his condition from me.* The thought crossed her mind. Her inability to believe that infidelity had found a home in her marriage caused Sam to dismiss the thought. She conveniently brushed aside her own unfaithfulness.

She took out her cell phone to call and curse out A'Man. Then she realized that she had never gotten his number, but she remembered where he lived.

No matter how she tried to brush aside the obligation to inform Andrew of the STD, the thought wouldn't go away. And rightly so, because she knew she had to do it. But she was apprehensive. *How do I come clean to a man who has a problem with his hands? I could lie and tell him that I was raped; but how would I explain having sex, let alone, letting Andrew give me oral?* Sam dismissed that thought for fear that Andrew could see through her lies.

Sam contemplated just waiting to see if Andrew developed any symptoms of his own and then telling him the truth. *I cheated because you kicked me in the butt.* That idea was also dismissed.

Sam's mind went into overdrive. She could get Andrew over to her doctor and have the doctor secretly test Andrew under the guise of testing him for something else. But her mind kept going back to the fact that once he learned that he had Gonorrhea. He would know she gave it to him, and it could be curtains for her.

Sam thought about the possibility of the doctor confirming that Andrew was burning. She could persuade the doctor to be silent, and she could crush up the prescribed medication and put it in his food. *Desperate situation call for desperate measures*, she thought.

After an hour or so of what ifs, Sam decided that she had to confront A'Man. As far as Andrew, she would remain silent and wait for the firestorm—if it ever came. She prayed all would be well on the home front.

As she stood to leave the theater, she had forgotten two small problems: where does she hide her medication, and what excuse could she use to avoid having sex with Andrew?

...

Andrew climbed out of bed still groggy from a pleasant night of sleep. Several times he yawned as he made his way to the bathroom. While he stood relaxed in front of the toilet holding his penis ready to urinate, he looked down and saw the pus-like, yellowish discharge that came from his urethra. Shocked, Andrew's body stiffened, except his heart, which punched at the interior of his chest.

"Shit!"

Regaining his ability to move, Andrew quickly checked his underwear and saw what he expected—the dry, pus-like, yellowish and greenish discharge that soiled a quarter-side section in his white drawers. Andrew closed his eyes and prayed that what he suspected wasn't the case.

Although it had been twenty-five years since Andrew went through this same experience, he remembered the symptoms quite well. Thanks to the embarrassing episode performed by his father in front of Andrew's three sisters and his mother.

Andrew recalled the events so vividly in his mind that one would think they happened yesterday rather than when he was fifteen years old.

It was a typical day. He went to pee and felt the burning sensation. He had gotten torched by the neighborhood whore. Shamefully, Andrew walked into his parent's room and told his mother that it burns when he peed. His mother told him to tell his father. Knowing his father had a flair for dramatics, Andrew pleaded with his mother to keep the matter between the two of them. But she insisted that Andrew tell his father.

He finally garnered the heart to tell his father. What happened next would stay with Andrew his entire life. Andrew's father assembled the family into the living room; then the father walked into the kitchen and retrieved a spoon, fork, plate, and a drinking glass. Everyone was bewildered until Andrew's father told the family that Andrew had caught the "Claps" and he was only to use the tableware that was placed before him. At that moment, Andrew felt like an illegal alien in the hands of INS. Fortunately for Andrew, his family disobeyed his father's orders.

Presently, with the urge to pee heightening, Andrew shook the memory of his past. He wished that he could hold his pee forever, but with a filled bladder, the inevitable was at hand.

Andrew took a deep breath, closed his eyes, and braced himself. Sure enough, when he urinated it felt like fire was shooting from his penis.

"Bitch! Stinking bitch!"

Andrew dragged himself back to the bedroom and sat on the bed, thinking he was in a world of shit. In typical fashion, Andrew—like most men who contracted an STD and had a woman on the side—developed instant tunnel vision, blaming the other woman. He refused to blame his better half, whom he couldn't bring himself to believe, would cheat on him.

...

Later that afternoon, A'Man left the health clinic dispirited and a little pissed, but given the circumstances, he wasn't terribly angry as he had been earlier. Maybe it was because he and Gonorrhea were old friends: several times throughout his late teens and adult life he had been treated for the disease, even as recently as six months ago.

As he drove slowly through traffic, he recounted the women whom he had had sexual relations with in the last couple of weeks. There were five, Sam being the fifth. He recalled using a condom only once or twice.

A'Man hated condoms. His view of safe sex was not getting caught in bed by the woman's husband or boyfriend. Consequently, this latest bout with an STD would have him rethink his view about wearing protection.

A'Man pulled to the curb a couple of parking spaces down from the house of the woman whom he suspected of burning him. Before he could exit the car, he saw what appeared to be a heated argument between the woman and a man in front of her house.

A'Man watched the confrontation for a moment and considered driving away until he saw that the woman had noticed him. Strangely, the woman didn't look particularly pleased to see him.

As A'Man continued to watch the argument from his car, the argument escalated into a shoving match with the woman being the aggressor.

"Is this bitch trying to get me in some shit?" A'Man asked himself.

A'Man sighed, and then hopped out of the car, taking his time to walk over to the incident.

"What's going on?" A'Man asked in an even voice, trying not to further agitate the man.

"Who the fuck are you?" the man asked, giving A'Man the look over.

"A'Man, just get back in your car. I'll call you later."

Before A'Man had a chance to speak, the man blared out, "Are you fucking him, too?"

"I don't answer to you!" said the woman. "A'Man, leave. I'll get with you later, baby."

The man chuckled, "Yo, dude, this bitch burned me!" said the man. "I'm just letting you know how she travel."

"Fuck you, pussy! How do I know you didn't give it to me?"

A'Man shook his head sadly at the woman. He had gotten his answer, so he walked back to his car and drove away.

• • •

It took several phone calls to family members and friends before Andrew was able to attain a babysitter on the spur of the moment. With a sense of urgency, he made the embarrassing trip to the health clinic. The same clinic where A'Man was being treated.

Ironically, while A'Man was leaving, he held open the door for Andrew as he entered the building. The two strangers exchanged a friendly nod as they proceeded on their way.

After his doctor visit, Andrew sat on the sofa in his girlfriend's living room. Although he appeared calm, his insides churned with rage. As he struck up a casual conversation with her, Andrew's intention was to subtly move the conversation to persuade his girlfriend to admit that she had cheated on him.

"This is a surprise visit. I'm happy to see you. What's going on, baby?" said the girlfriend as she tidied up the messy living room and adjoining dining room.

"Nothing, I just wanted to see you."

"Are you sure, because you don't look too well."

"I'm cool. Just going through a lot of shit with Sam. We got into another fight this morning."

"Why are you still playing games with that bitch? Leave her like you said you were going to do. What's taking you so long? I thought you wanted to be with me and our son."

"I do, baby, but it's difficult to just walk out on my children."

"What were you and that bitch arguing about?" Andrew hesitated, "She just admitted that she cheated on me in the past."

Andrew intentionally lied; his motive was simple, gauge his girlfriend's reaction to the fact that he had been cheated on. He watched her closely, but there was no break in her movement, nor did she respond.

"I told her to always be honest with me and we could get through anything. If somebody lies, the truth will surface sooner or later."

"Well, how could you blame her for cheating? Shit, you're cheating on her with me or me with her. It's been so long I don't know who's one or number two anymore."

"So you condone cheating?"

"I'm just saying...fuck what Sam does. I can't stand that nasty bitch."

Clearly, the girlfriend was attempting to assassinate Sam's character to trigger a reaction from Andrew, who peeped her game. He decided to reverse the charges on her, keeping her on the defensive.

"So in essence, you're saying if I cheated, Sam has the right to do her thing?"

"What the fuck are you interrogating me for? Look, if you came over here to get on my nerves, I don't have time for it. You can go back home to that sorry bitch and argue with her. She's the one who cheated on you. I've been waiting for you for four years!"

"What are you trying to say?"

"I'm not trying to say shit. I'm just stating a fact. Men are all the same. Y'all want your cake and eat it, too."

"What about women?"

"Stop questioning me!"

Andrew's antennas hit the ceiling. Twice, his girlfriend had hollered about being questioned. Andrew attributed her outburst to guilt, so he decided to stop pussyfooting around and get straight to the point.

"Who are you fucking?"

The girlfriend stopped. She was paralyzed with surprise, but Andrew noticed that she didn't look taken aback.

"Who told you that?" she said in a guilty voice.

"Someone told me that they just saw you --"

"That bitch down the street needs to mind her damn business. She don't know what the fuck she's talking about."

With a sudden queasiness of the stomach, Andrew stood slowly on weakened legs, his face a portrait of hurt. Although the girlfriend tried to avoid looking in his direction, ever so often she would glance at him.

"I think that bitch likes you anyway. I remember something she mentioned a long time ago that I picked up. I'm not stupid. Did she ever say anything to you?"

"Who the dude?"

"What dude?"

"Stop playing dumb! The motherfucker you're sneaking around with!"

"You and your wife get in a fight and you bring the bullshit over here."

"Who is he?"

"We just went out to dinner the other night, no big deal. You couldn't take me out because you were with your kids and that bitch," the girlfriend added sarcastically.

"So are you sneaking around?"

"I wasn't sneaking. I walked out of my house and got in his car, which was parked in front of my door," the girlfriend said cockily.

Andrew thought about smacking her in her sassy mouth. But unlike with Sam, he had never laid a hand on his girlfriend, who didn't know or wouldn't believe he had a violent streak.

"You fucking bitch!"

"Your funky wife is a bitch! So save your bitches for her, okay."

Andrew chuckled, "You ain't shit. I pay your rent, take care of my son, and you're out there fucking with dudes."

"I'm not trying to hear this! You have a wife and I'm supposed to sit back and wait until you get ready to leave her. Cyrek said you weren't going to leave her."

Although the secret was out that the girlfriend was cheating, putting a name to the mystery man was an insult to Andrew's injured heart.

"Who the fuck is Cyrek?"

"Cyrek said if you loved me, you would be here every night."

"Fuck Cy – whatever! Are you're fucking him?"

"I told you, don't question me. Question your wife."

"Are you fucking him?" Andrew screamed at the top of his voice.

"Yes," the girlfriend said calm and coldly.

Andrew looked crushed. He wiped his hands over his face while the girlfriend stood impassively with her lips poked out and her hands on her hips. The cold-hearted revelation prompted Andrew to believe that there had been others in her past.

"How many guys have you been with since dealing with me?"

"I'm not a whore. Sam's the whore. Like I said, question that bitch."

"You're right...where is my son?"

"He's with Cyrek."

"Bitch, I should kick your ass!"

"Put your hands on me and see what happens."

The girlfriend walked to a safe distance on the other side of the room.

"You got my son out in the street with another motherfucker. Call your boyfriend?"

"No."

The bitch didn't deny that he was her boyfriend, Andrew thought as he walked over and stood in front of his girlfriend. She looked poise for a fight.

"You better not touch me."

"How long have you been seeing this cat?"

The girlfriend hesitated, "He's not a cat, he's a man, and I've been dating him on and off for four and a half years."

This time Andrew couldn't hold back. He slapped her hard across her face. She looked ruffled as the spunkiness abandoned her.

"Get the fuck out!"

"I want my son!"

"Get out of here!"

"Not until I see my damn son!"

"Well, go the fuck home and look at Sam's son, if he's yours!"

"What?"

"My son is not yours! Cyrek took the DNA test!"

It looked like the life drained from Andrew. His legs felt wobbly, but his anger was strong, and the girlfriend saw it.

"Get the fuck out! You don't have shit here!"

With tears in his eyes, Andrew wrapped his hands around his girlfriend's neck, choking her without thought for her life. If it wasn't for the ringing of the telephone that caused Andrew to catch himself, he would've possibly committed murder.

"You're not worth it," said Andrew, releasing his grip from her neck.

"I hate you. I'm going to call your wife and tell her everything!"

FRIENDS

"Keep running your mouth and I'm going to break your jaw."

It was the sincerity in Andrew's voice that convinced the girlfriend that he would follow through with the threat. So she moved to the sofa and sat quietly, hoping that he would leave without further violence. Andrew looked at her for a moment, then left.

...

When Sam arrived home, she was surprised to find her teenage neighbor babysitting the children. Paranoia rushed through Sam's body. She questioned the sitter, asking if Andrew had mentioned where he was going. All the sitter could offer was that Andrew looked worried and that he left in a hurry. Sam paid the sitter and sent her on her way.

Without a shadow of a doubt, Sam knew Andrew was at the clinic. She also knew that it would be no avoiding or delaying telling Andrew about the affair. She debated whether to call him, but she didn't have the guts to deliver that kind of heartbreak over the phone, even though it would be safer.

Sam sat at the kitchen table, wondering how much time she had before he came home. She contemplated how she would begin. After mulling over several openings, she just decided to start from him kicking her in the butt and let the chips fall where they may.

Twenty minutes later, Sam was in the living room with the children when Andrew walked through the door. The first thing she noticed was his eyes. She had never seen them so sad. She also noticed the white pharmacy bag he was holding.

Andrew didn't speak. He told the children in a stern voice to go to their room and stay there until he told them to come out. He also told Sam they needed to talk when he came from the bathroom. Sam felt sick but tried to keep a stable face.

While Andrew was upstairs in the bathroom, Sam paced the room trembling. Aside from her marriage being on the brink of finality, she knew that she could end up in the emergency room, or worse.

Shortly after going upstairs, Andrew descended the stairs slowly. As Sam watched him, suddenly she wasn't afraid anymore. She walked boldly toward Andrew, stopping him at the bottom of the stairs.

"Andrew --"

"Wait Sam," Andrew interrupted.

"No, let me say what I have to say --"

"Why do you always have to be the one with the first word? Let me get this out."

Sam sat quietly on the sofa and folded her hands, resting them on her lap. Andrew stood before her.

"I don't know how to say this," Andrew said with tears welling in his eyes, "I have Gonorrhea and I probably burned you."

Andrew looked down at Sam, whose eyes didn't blink as she stared back at him, thankful that she held her tongue and allowed him to speak first. When she didn't immediately reply, Andrew figured that she was in shock. He sat next to her and reached for her hand. She snatched it back.

"I'm sorry, but I cheated," Andrew said.

Although she was devastated by the news of Andrew's betrayal, Sam felt relieved that she didn't have to come clean about her own affair. She decided to take advantage of the moment.

In a slow and methodical voice, Sam said, "Damn near everyday for the last few years you accused me of sleeping around. All I did in life was go to work, come home, cook, clean, and take care of the kids. When I was tired or sick, I gave you my body. I have never been unfaithful. Now you tell me that you cheated and that I might have a disease."

Sam surprised herself by how well the lies flowed from her lips.

"I'm sorry. I want to tell you everything."

"You hit me and kicked me in the ass. How do you think that made me feel; not only as a woman, but a human being?"

"I'm sorry, baby."

"You even disrespect me in front of the kids," Sam said with tears in her eyes. "Who is the woman?"

A steady flow of tears fell from Andrew's eyes as he disclosed everything about his four-year affair. With her heart in a million pieces, Sam listened quietly. When Andrew was finished, Sam stood up, wiped her tears away, and grabbed her car keys, leaving the house without saying a word.

Andrew didn't bother to chase her. He assumed she was headed to the clinic. Little did he know, she was just going to drive around to clear her mind and to allow him to wallow in his misery.

Who would've thought that infidelity and an STD would repair a broken marriage?

CHAPTER

5

It was three o'clock on a gloomy Wednesday afternoon. Up until that point, the best part of the day for a weary Tracy was when the doorman held open the door for her as she exited the office building from, yet, another unsuccessful job interview.

Day after day, Tracy had been on several interviews since she was fired, and after each interview, she felt like she had the word VETO stamped to her forehead. With each interview, the same routine transpired: she was complimented on being well spoken, the companies always liked her "look" but her lack of education—lack of experience or no experience—translated to the usual phrase, "Sorry, we're looking for someone with more experience."

Tracy climbed inside of her Pathfinder, wishing she could turn back time. Sixteen years to be exact. After wasting a few minutes of wishing for the impossible, Tracy scanned the interior of the vehicle, wondering how she would be able to keep up the car note and insurance.

Sure, she could find minimum-wage employment, but that income alone wouldn't be enough to pay for child care, bills, car payments, and other odds and ends. Tracy shook her head, chuckling while thinking, *this always happens to me.*

Out of the blue, Tracy thought about stripping. Instantly, the inner conflict began. She noted that the money would suffice her needs, but whether or not she could crawl back into that world was a big question mark.

She had tried stripping five years ago, only lasting a week because she lacked the stomach for shaking her ass in front of strangers.

As Tracy sat idly, pondering her next move, Sam popped in her mind, leaving Tracy to wonder why she hadn't been answering her phone. Tracy picked up her cell and punched Sam's number, only to get her voicemail. "Damn, what's up with you girl?" Tracy said, leaving the message on Sam's voicemail.

Ready to put down her phone, Tracy paused, then she placed a call to Dawn, inquiring about the five hundred dollars Dawn promised to loan her.

Although Dawn stated that she was too busy to talk, she told Tracy to stop by the office in an hour to pick up the money. *Finally, some good news.*

As Tracy pulled into traffic with no specific destination, she decided to drive around awhile to kill time. That was until she remembered the price of gas and nixed the idea.

On an impulse, Tracy made a U-turn, almost causing an accident. She headed to a place that she vowed she would never step foot in again in her life.

Five minutes later, she pulled into the parking lot at the strip club where she used to work. Nervously, she walked through the door of the club that was fairly empty. Tracy first looked to the stage. Everything was the same, save the unknown face of a pretty girl on the stage dancing for one customer.

"Tracy!" The manager of the club shouted.

Tracy looked startled until she saw the husky and handsome manager heading in her direction with a smile.

"Hi," Tracy said, managing a smile of her own.

As the pair embraced, the manager squeezed her tightly and took his time letting go. Tracy had to give him a friendly pat on the back to encourage him to release her. The manager took a step back to look Tracy up and down.

"Umm, girl, you still look the same."

"You too."

"What are you doing here, baby girl?"

"I need to work."

"The last time I saw you, you said you'd never work in this fucking place again in your life."

"Well, you know, circumstances change."

"I heard you had a daughter. How's she doing?"

"Fine."

"That's good...I missed you."

"Can I get some work or what?"

"Do you think of me sometimes?"

"Well?"

"Can you shake that pretty ass without your whole body trembling?"

"Can I get a job or what?"

As the manager took his time to respond, he saw the desperation in Tracy's eyes. He looked at her closely just to determine if she had become a drug user. Satisfied that he didn't see any noticeable traces of being an addict, he smiled. Tracy always loved when he used to flash his pearly whites on her. But now they didn't move her, she was there for work.

"Well?"

"You know I love you, girl. When do you want to come in?"

"Tomorrow."

"Sure...what are you doing tonight?"

"We been there, done that."

"Don't front, girl. You know we had a good time."

"So did you and a bunch of other bitches on my watch."

"You have to go there?"

"You're right. I'll see you tomorrow, thank you."

"Don't I get a kiss on the cheek?"

"I no longer mix business with pleasure," Tracy said with a smile as she left the club.

As she drove to meet Dawn, she told herself she would dance for a month just to get caught up with her bills and put something in her savings.

Twenty minutes later, Tracy stood in front of the desk of a receptionist at Dawn's law firm. Tracy was shaking her head in angry disbelief.

The receptionist had just handed Tracy an envelope left by Dawn, who left the building forty minutes earlier for the night.

The envelope contained seventy-five dollars. Tracy told the receptionist that it was supposed to be five hundred. The receptionist responded that she never looked inside the envelope, and the only message from Dawn was that a friend would stop by. When she does, just give her the envelope.

Tracy left the building irate. She hopped in her car and smacked the steering wheel repeatedly before she started the car.

As she sped through the parking lot, she was blinded with rage and failed to negotiate a turn in time and crashed into a concrete pillar, subsequently breaking her arm.

• • •

In a nearby restaurant, Dawn sat across the table from Dave. The pair gazed into each other's eyes like young lovers on their second date.

"I love you, David."

Before Dave could respond, Dawn's cell phone rang. She looked at the number on the phone and sighed, allowing the call to go her voicemail.

"That was you're friend again?"

"Yeah, she so darn needy. I left money for her."

"Maybe she has an emergency."

"She always has an emergency. But you are more important, baby, that's why I'm not answering."

"When a neighbor told me that you were sitting on the floor outside my apartment, all the anger I had for you just vanished...I still want to be that power couple."

"Me, too. That's why I never gave up on you."

The pair leaned across the table and kissed. After an hour of professing their love for each other, the pair embraced, kissed each other goodbye, and hopped into their cars and drove to their respective homes.

When Dawn arrived home she was on cloud nine. She could think of nothing but David and how handsome she thought he looked tonight. As she sashayed towards her front door, she saw an angry looking Tracy with her arm in a sling.

When Dawn got closer to Tracy, she saw the cast on her arm. Dawn placed her hand on her mouth and jogged over to Tracy.

"Oh my God, what happened to you?"

"Why did you tell me to meet you at your office when you knew you weren't going to be there?"

"Let's go inside. I'll make some tea."

"I don't want no damn tea!"

"Well, come in anyway."

Once inside Dawn's apartment, Tracy and Dawn sat on the sofa.

"Where were you at?"

"You didn't get my message?"

"Seventy-five dollars? What happened to the five hundred?"

"All the cash I had on me was seventy-five dollars. I gave it to the receptionist and told her to tell you that I was going to write you a check for the rest."

"Why didn't you leave the check?"

"I didn't have my checkbook."

Tracy gave Dawn a look.

"You think I'm lying?"

Tracy thought for a moment, "No, I'm just mad as shit."

"What happened to your arm?"

"Mad at you and speeding."

Dawn stood, brushing aside what Tracy had said as irrelevant.

"David and I are back together."

"That's why my arm is broken because you left me stranded to be with him?"

"Of course not. I had to meet a client to get a deposition."

That response elicited another suspicious look from Tracy. At this point, Dawn didn't care how Tracy felt.

"Listen, it's getting late and I have to pick up Tammy. Let me get the check so I can get out of here."

"Not a problem," said Dawn as she pulled out her checkbook. "I think David and I are going to make it."

Tracy rolled her eyes out of view of Dawn as she listened to Dawn continue to yap about herself and Dave.

"I don't know when I'll be able to pay you back, but once I get a job…"

As Dawn handed the check to Tracy, she said, "I'm not worried about this little couple of dollars…friendship needs to be tested, right?"

Tracy didn't answer. She took the check thinking, *this bitch really knows how to rub it in.*

Later that night, Tracy stood in her bedroom staring at herself in the mirror. She looked at her broken arm thinking it's impossible to strip to now. She was thinking some perverted men might believe it's sexy to watch a chick with a broken arm stripping.

Faced with what seemed to be a continuous problem, Tracy climbed in bed and stared at the ceiling, wondering what she was going to do now. To make matters worse, it would take Tracy awhile to get used to sleeping with a broken arm.

CHAPTER

6

Two months after being arrested on assault charges against Joann, Tracy, with her arm in a sling, stood nervously at the defense table, awaiting the judge's ruling. At Tracy's side stood an overly confident-looking Dawn, who was also Tracy's defense attorney. Sam sat in the gallery of the empty courtroom for moral support. Spying on the proceeding from the back of the gallery was Rob. He had eased into the room unnoticed by the girls. He was there to ensure things went according to plan. It had taken several weeks of persuasion and catering to her desires before Joann finally agreed not to testify against Tracy.

While the district attorney was making his statement to the court, Tracy felt like she was in a foreign land. The room was too cold for her comfort, and the legal jargon the D.A. spoke could've been in Chinese as far as Tracy was concerned, because all she understood was the mentioning of her name and the need for a postponement to secure Joann's appearance.

After the D.A. had his say, the hearing took less than ten minutes for the stern-faced judge to declare the case dismissed due to lack of evidence—thanks to Joann's failure to attend the proceeding and provide testimony against Tracy.

Upon the judge's ruling, Rob eased out of the courtroom in the same manner in which he came, unnoticed.

Tracy let out a sigh of relief as she embraced Dawn. Sam stayed seated and thanked God for the outcome of the case.

Looking triumphant, as if she had just gotten Tracy acquitted of committing the crime of the century, Dawn clenched Tracy's hand and led her proudly out of the courtroom. Sam followed behind them at a considerable distance.

In the Criminal Justice Center hallway, Dawn boasted to Tracy about winning her first case. Dawn even did a quick victory dance that she had practiced the night before in anticipation of this moment. Being as though Tracy was so elated that the ordeal was finally over, she didn't remind Dawn that the case was won the moment Joann agreed not to show up for court.

Standing a few yards away, Sam watched Tracy and Dawn from the sideline. She would've been at the center of the celebration, but since the incident that occurred at Tracy's house, Dawn and Sam's relationship was still strained, and Tracy was sick of it. It was time to bring the friends together, so Tracy waved Sam over.

In accord with her stubbornness, Sam walked unhurriedly over to the girls and stood next to Tracy, who looked dissatisfied.

"This ends today," said Tracy, looking first to Sam, then to Dawn.

With her free hand, Tracy motioned Sam to take a step towards Dawn. Sam did so reluctantly. As Sam and Dawn stood face to face, both women avoided making eye contact with each other.

"Sam, we argue with one another all the time. You and me, you and Dawn, Dawn and me. But we never raise our hands…"

Sam opened her mouth to speak, but Tracy held up her own hand cutting her off.

Tracy continued, "Sam, you crossed the line and should apologize. Forget whatever smart thing Dawn may have said to provoke you, it doesn't matter. You had no right to put your hands on her. It's only right that you apologize so we can move on."

Not ready to abandon her stubborn position, Sam stood quietly, wrestling with the idea of whether or not to let bygones be bygones. She thought about her present life and how everything was moving in a positive direction: she was working, the children were fine and Andrew had been the perfect husband, making up for those years of mistreating her.

"I apologize for choking you, Dawn."

"I'm sorry too, Aunt Sammy," said Dawn with a grin.

With smiles all around, Dawn and Sam embraced with Tracy putting her outstretched arms around the both of them.

"Friends," Tracy said.

When the girls tore themselves from each other, Tracy said, "We should go celebrate. I can afford sodas and one sandwich without cheese for each of us. Y'all have to buy your own chips."

"Don't worry, I got it," Sam offered.

"I can't go. I have to be in another courtroom in a few minutes," Dawn said, glancing at her watch.

Sam made a face that was observed only by Tracy. Knowing that Sam was ready to start an argument, Tracy shook her head "no."

"I took off work today and --" Sam said, then she paused.

Sam was about to finish her sentence with a sarcastic remark but changed her mind about picking a fight.

"I guess we can do something this weekend," Tracy said.

"Yeah...we should go out clubbing. We haven't been out in a long time."

"Alright," Tracy agreed.

"I left something in the courtroom. I'll give y'all a call later," Dawn said.

After the women said their goodbyes, Dawn went back into the courtroom. Tracy and Sam headed out of the building. If they would've stayed inside a minute longer, they would've bumped into A'Man, who was walking down the hall with Mr. Hall.

When Dawn emerged from the courtroom, she ran into A'Man and Mr. Hall. Both men didn't look particularly happy, but their facial expressions changed when they saw Dawn.

"Mr. Hall. Hey, how are you doing?" Dawn said surprisingly.

"I've been better. You remember A'Man?"

"Yes," Dawn said.

Dawn gave A'Man a quick look over out the corner of her eye. But nothing too obvious that would get his attention or offend Mr. Hall.

"You look pretty chipper," Mr. Hall said.

"I feel terrific."

"I assume you won a victory for your friend?"

"Yes."

"I knew it was a slam dunk with you on the case."

Dawn felt flattered and showed it with a wide smile. A'Man took notice of her well-kept, white teeth and thought it was her smile that made Dawn appealing, if she was cute at all.

"How did your case go?" Dawn asked.

"Unfortunately, we were ambushed with some damaging evidence," Mr. Hall said disappointedly.

A'Man lowered his head shamefully. Two lawyers standing a few yards away noticed Mr. Hall. One of the lawyers got Mr. Hall's attention and waved him over.

"Give me a second, I need to speak with those gentlemen," Mr. Hall said.

As Mr. Hall chatted with his two colleagues, Dawn felt awkward while avoiding eye contact with A'Man who was staring at her.

"So you beat your case?" A'Man asked.

"Yes, my first victory," said Dawn shyly.

Dawn wasn't particularly shy, but A'Man's good looks and confidence made her a bit bashful.

"Was it a murder?"

"Nothing like that, an aggravated assault."

"Wow, maybe I should've had you on my case."

Dawn gloated inside but controlled her delight by only flashing a quick smile to show her appreciation for the compliment.

"You were in good hands. It had to be the new evidence."

"I guess so."

After their chit-chat, Dawn and A'Man ran out of things to say. During their silence, their eyes met a couple of times. It was during those meeting of the eyes that something happened between them, but it wasn't addressed because Mr. Hall had returned.

"I apologize for the interruption. Where were we?"

"Just discussing my victory, but later for that. I have to run. I'll see you back at the office."

"Okay."

Dawn nodded goodbye to A'Man and walked away. Mr. Hall and A'Man headed in the opposite direction. Then, before Dawn and A'Man were out of eyesight of each other, they both looked back over their shoulders at precisely the same moment, locking eyes briefly before continuing on their way.

• • •

Tracy and Sam stopped in a fast-food restaurant, taking a seat near the window. Despite her financial situation, Tracy insisted on paying for lunch.

"Dawn was behaving like she got you off of death row," Sam said.

"It was her first case, so she was just happy."

"If it wasn't for Rob convincing Joann to do the right thing, we would've seen how good an attorney Dawn really is. Even though this shit was Rob's fault in the first place."

"That's all behind me. Let's talk about something else. Like that rock on your finger," Tracy said, pointing to Sam's new diamond ring.

"Just something Andrew bought me last week."

"What did you give him?" Tracy said, raising an inquiring eyebrow."

Sam laughed and placed her fist in front of her mouth, simulating a blow job.

"Stop that, it's kids in here!"

"Shit, I'm sure they probably seen mommy take care of daddy."

They both laughed.

"I'm happy y'all are doing well"

"Me, too, since the --" Sam paused, catching herself.

"Since what?"

"Since we put everything out on the table, the marriage is good again. We're having fun like we did when I was a young girl sneaking around with him."

Sam had never revealed to anyone the ordeal with the infidelity and the STD. She and Andrew decided to keep it that way.

"Why can't I find a good man?"

"You know where they say all the good ones are at."

"If they were so good, they wouldn't be locked up."

"I'm not going to challenge that one. Have you heard anything from Steve lately?"

"No. My mother has been talking to him though. Leave it to her to collaborate with the enemy...but I was thinking about letting him see Tammy at least once a week. Besides his initial denial of her, he's not a bad dude."

"What about him going to court?"

Upon hearing that, Tracy's mood changed.

"I said let's talk about pleasant things. Today is the start of my new life."

"Well, I like my new job."

"I hate my job. Waiting on tables with this thing on my arm. I have to get something else, my bills are piling up."

"I'm going to have some money for you this weekend."

"Thanks, I still owe Dawn a nickel."

"You don't have to pay me back. I'm a true friend."

Tracy didn't respond. She was just thinking how grateful she was to have Sam as a friend. In spite of Dawn being the cause of a few of her troubles, Tracy was even grateful that Dawn was her friend as well.

"I'll be back, I have to go to the bathroom," said Sam as she stood.

While Sam was in the bathroom, Sam and Tracy's ex-supervisor Anthony was walking by the restaurant. He stopped when he looked through the window and saw Tracy sitting alone. Anthony entered the restaurant and strolled over to the table were Tracy was sitting, surprising her.

"Hey, Tracy."

"Hello."

"I just stopped by to say hello."

"Hello."

"What happened to your arm?"

"An accident."

"Well, like I said, I just wanted to say hello. Are you working?"

"Yes."

"That's good...well, you take care. I'm sorry things didn't work out at the job, but you know there are people other than me who are really in charge."

Tracy thought, *yeah, but you do the hiring and firing.*

"Well, you got my number, give me a call sometimes. Take it easy," Anthony said.

Anthony gave Tracy the eye for a moment to let her know he was still interested in her. Tracy recognized the look but ignored it.

"You take it easy, too, bye."

When Anthony walked away, Tracy didn't give him to much of a thought. Moments later, Sam returned. Tracy started to tell her about the encounter with Anthony but kept it to herself

FRIENDS

...

An hour after leaving the courthouse, Dawn was still beaming from her court victory. She decided to detour from heading to the law firm so she could share the news of her first win with Dave.

Dave had his own practice where he employed a paralegal and a beautiful legal assistant, who doubled as his receptionist. When Dawn entered Dave's law office suite, she told the receptionist to let Dave know she was waiting.

Dawn and the receptionist knew each other and always shared pleasantries when they were in each other's company, but today the receptionist seemed to have an attitude. Dawn figured Dave had probably told her about the abortion.

Dawn entered Dave's office and embraced him tightly. Dave looked surprised by the greeting.

"What's up?"

"I won my first case!"

"That's terrific," Dave said, closing the door.

"I feel exhilarated. I just wanted to stop by and thank my lover and mentor. Besides my grateful client, you are the first to know about my victory."

"I'm honored."

Dawn removed the cushion from the chair. She dropped it in front of Dave.

"What are you doing?"

"I object to your question counselor. Close your mouth and observe the proceeding."

Dave did as instructed. Dawn dropped to her knees on the cushion and began servicing Dave. As he enjoyed the pleasure, he prayed that his receptionist didn't walk in.

When Dawn was finished, she replaced the cushion, kissed Dave on his cheek, and then left the office without saying a word. As Dave stretched and smiled with satisfaction, his stomach growled from a sudden appetite. Dave chuckled and thought, *well, she had her lunch.*

...

Later that evening in a posh hotel room, Mr. Hall lay on the bed, stripped down to his boxers. His lusty grin could barely be seen in the semi-darkened room.

He removed his hands from tapping his chest lightly and rested them behind his head while he waited. His wait wasn't long. He could smell Dawn's perfume as she exited the bathroom clad in an expensive bathrobe. She walked over to the front of the bed and stood with her hands on her hips and her legs spread apart. Mr. Hall rose up and shook his head slowly in admiration while gazing at his mistress.

"You are absolutely beautiful."

Dawn smiled appreciatively. No matter how often Mr. Hall complimented her on her beauty, it was like she was hearing it for the first time.

She slowly began to move her hips from side to side; her body was flowing to a tune in her mind. As she danced seductively, Mr. Hall's eyes grew with excitement and hunger. His hunger for her was like no man before him. Dawn felt proud that she had the sexual prowess to make a married man desire her like she was the only woman on earth.

"Come here, baby," Mr. Hall said, moving to the edge of the bed.

Dawn danced slowly towards him. He stood up and undid her belt. She let the robe fall to the floor. Mr. Hall moved back a bit to observe her naked body.

He stood while placing his left hand on her waist and taking her left hand in his right hand as he proceeded to guide her in a slow waltz. The couple danced to a rhythm in their own minds. Their moves were in sync like they had danced across this floor a hundred times before.

Moments later, Mr. Hall led Dawn to the bed where he helped her lie down on her back. She closed her eyes and grinned licentiously as he crawled between her legs. She let out a moan of ecstasy when he touched her with his tongue.

As the pleasure continued, thoughts of Dave sneaked their way into Dawn's mind. She tried to dismiss him, but he was stubborn. For the first time in their many trysts, Dawn felt guilty for betraying Dave.

When Mr. Hall finished servicing Dawn, he lay on his back. Dawn kissed his chest and his neck with soft, wet kisses. She sat next to him, rubbing her warm hand across his hairy chest.

"Come on baby," Mr. Hall said.

Dawn clenched Mr. Hall's penis, slowly beginning to masturbate him.

"Come on, baby. Do it."

With her free hand, she gave a light punch to Mr. Hall's chest. He moaned in pleasure.

"Yes, yes," said Mr. Hall.

Dawn quickened her hand job and delivered more impact to her punches.

"Do it, baby, do it, baby!"

Dave face's popped in her mind. She hit Mr. Hall harder and harder. He loved it. Outside of her affection for Mr. Hall, Dawn wondered if his influence over her future was worth the effort.

"Oh my, baby. Ooh baby!"

Mr. Hall grunted. His body jerked as he released on Dawn's hand. This was how their rendezvous always ended. During their many get-togethers, one thing never occurred, penis and vaginal intercourse. That was fine with Dawn, and she never asked why.

As she lay in his arms, she wondered how long she would be able to keep this going, now that she was falling in love with Dave.

...

After finishing her shift and picking up Tammy from the sitter, Tracy parked the Pathfinder four blocks away from her house to avoid the repo-man. She would straighten out the car payments when Sam gave her money. Until then, she had to play it safe.

When Tammy asked why did they always have to walk so far to their house, Tracy would tell her they needed the exercise.

As Tracy entered the house, she stepped on the mail lying on the floor. She picked up the envelopes and glanced at them, already knowing that they were bills and shut-off notices. She flopped down on the couch thinking, *I have to do something.*

CHAPTER
7

The nightclub was packed with a sea of party-goers sweating up the dance floor. This trendy club was the night spot for the twenty-and thirty-something bourgeois crowd and those who like to party with them.

After dancing together for a couple of songs, Dawn and Tracy ordered drinks and retired to a table. Sam wasn't feeling well and had decided to stay at home, which worked for Tracy since Sam offered to let Tammy sleep over with her children.

This was Tracy's first time at this particular club. Although this wasn't her scene or choice of people to party with, she was having a good time.

"You're having fun, aren't you?" Dawn said, shouting over the music.

"I can't complain."

"If it was up to you and Sam, we'd probably be in some neighborhood speakeasy with some whiskey-breath old men trying to get into our pants."

"I'm not going to feed."

"I'm just joking. The guys in here are professionals. These are the kind of men you should be hooking up with."

"The last time you played matchmaker, we both know what happened."

The reference to Rob shut Dawn up instantly. There was nothing she could say to defend that short-lived hookup with Rob. Dawn and Tracy sat quietly nursing their drinks and bobbing their heads to the heavy drumbeat vibrating their eardrums.

For a second, Tracy thought she had saw Dave as her eyes roamed the crowd. She did a double take, and indeed, her eyes had not deceived her. Dave was on the dance floor, but he wasn't dancing though. He appeared to be looking for someone.

"Dave is here," Tracy shouted as she pointed in his direction.

"Where?"

Dawn looked to where Tracy was pointing and saw Dave. He was still apparently searching for someone. Dawn's initial reaction was a cross between surprise and a feeling of deceit. Earlier that day, Dawn had asked Dave what were his plans for the evening. Dave responded that he was going to stay at home and critique a legal brief.

"Does he know we're here?"

Dawn shook her head "no," picked up her drink, and gulped it down.

"Go holler at him."

"He said he was staying at home to catch up on some work."

"I'm going to tell him we're over here."

Dawn reached out and clenched Tracy's arm to stop her. Tracy looked perplexed but didn't question Dawn's action.

"I'm going to watch his lying ass."

"Who do you think he's looking for?"

Dawn didn't answer. She sat back in her seat with an insidious smile. Tracy sat down, also. Neither woman said a word as they observed Dave's every move. While Dawn's intuition told her that Dave was up to no good, her suspicions were challenged by her need to trust him. There was no doubt in Tracy's distrustful mind what Dave was up to.

As Dave continued to search the club, his eyes widened with delight when he spotted his person of interest, who seemed to be making their way through the crowd. Dave waved his hand over his head so he would be noticed. Dawn stood abruptly and shot a look in the direction where Dave was focusing.

Dawn felt queasiness in her stomach when she saw Dave's receptionist, who looked stunning in a sleeveless dress with a plunging neckline, showcasing her incredible cleavage.

"What's wrong?" said Tracy.

Dawn couldn't speak; jealousy and betrayal high-jacked her tongue. She sucked her teeth and rolled her eyes at the sight of Dave hugging the receptionist. Tracy looked in the midst of the crowd and witnessed the embrace. Although she shook her head in disgust, she wasn't shocked.

"Forget him!" Tracy shouted.

Dawn, whose tongue was still in a knot, didn't say a word. She thought about her relationship with Mr. Hall and wondered whether the receptionist was sleeping with Dave to further her career.

Dawn picked up her empty glass and placed it to her mouth to drink until she realized the glass was empty. That minor mishap further swelled her anger.

Feeling her girlfriend's pain, Tracy sat down and searched for something to say. But from her own experience in this situation, she knew that there wasn't too much one could say, so she said, "Let's just leave."

As Dawn weighed her options, her eyes grew wide. She said excitedly, "They're headed in this direction!"

Dave, with the receptionist under his arm, was making his way through the crowd, unknowingly walking in the direction of Dawn and Tracy. When the happy couple was a few feet away from Dawn and Tracy, it was the receptionist who was first to see Dawn. The receptionist stopped, patted Dave on his chest, and pointed at her rival. Dave looked forward and cursed when he saw Dawn glaring at him. Tracy glared at the receptionist, but inside, Tracy was admiring the woman's dress.

"What the fuck is this?" Dawn yelled.

"What are you doing here?" Dave stuttered.

"No, what are you doing here? You told me that you were staying home tonight."

"Baby, let's just leave," the receptionist said.

When the receptionist pulled on Dave's arm, Dawn spotted the engagement ring on the receptionist's finger. Dawn's heart was broken. She now realized why the receptionist had an attitude the other day when she visited Dave.

"Are you fucking this bitch?" Dawn asked.

"Who are you fucking?" the receptionist said.

The receptionist gave Dawn a look that suggested, *I know your secret.* Dawn hesitated. She looked stunned as she wondered if Dave had found out about her affair with Mr. Hall and ran to the awaiting arms of the receptionist.

"Dawn, I'll call you later," Dave said.

Before Dawn could respond, Dave and the receptionist walked away, heading towards the exit. Dawn stood flatfooted in place with her shoulders hunched, acknowledging the grim reality that she had lost her man.

"Dawn, let's get out of here. It's obvious he wants to be with her."

"You're right."

Moments after Dave and the receptionist left the club, Dawn and Tracy followed them out of the door. Although the weather was cold, the chilly night air wasn't enough to cool Dawn's anger.

As Dave and his receptionist walked through the parking lot, Dawn made up her mind that she wasn't going to just let them walk away. Without warning, she gave chase, catching the cheaters before they reached Dave's car. Dawn dragged the receptionist to the ground by her hair and was able to rip the woman's dress almost completely off of her. Dawn even got in a few punches before the scuffle was broken up by Dave and Tracy.

"Dawn, it's not worth it!" Tracy yelled.

"No, that bitch isn't going to make me look like a fool."

"You're acting like one!" said the receptionist, covering her exposed breast with her arms.

As Tracy restrained the ranting and raving Dawn, Dave pulled the yelling and screaming receptionist to his car and drove away. Dawn picked up a bottle and hurled it at the departing car, just missing it.

"Fuck him, Dawn. When a man cheats, let him go."

"I'm fired up! That bitch got me heated!"

Dawn spotted two female onlookers standing nearby smirking. Dawn gave them the finger.

"What are y'all bitches looking at?" Dawn shouted.

The women—who were feeling the effects from the alcohol they had consumed—were more than happy to oblige Dawn in a fight, and Tracy could see it in their faces.

"You better walk away you little ugly bitch!" the woman closest to Dawn said.

"She apologizes, it's cool," Tracy intervened.

"Fuck them!"

"Dawn, I don't have time for this, let's go home."

"Alright," Dawn said.

"She's just mad because dude left with the other chick."

Before Tracy knew what happened, Dawn charged the two women in a fury of rage. Unfortunately, her brazen attack would leave her biting off more than she could chew. In a matter of seconds, Dawn was on the ground being stomped by her two assaulters. Tracy cursed in frustration as she rushed to Dawn's aide. In the heat of the melee, someone grabbed Tracy from behind. Without looking back, Tracy swung backwards, catching a female officer in her face.

When the smoke settled, Dawn and Tracy were thrown into separate patrol cars. As Tracy was being transported to the police station, she pleaded with the officers that her actions were a mistake and that she didn't realize that it was a cop who had grabbed her from behind.

The female officer that Tracy had hit was a hard-ass and unmoved by Tracy's tearful pleas.

After arriving at the station and being fingerprinted and booked on charges, Dawn and Tracy were placed in the same holding cell.

While Dawn walked around the holding cell hollering about Dave and the receptionist, Tracy sat quietly on the bench sobbing. All Tracy could think about was what was going to happen to Tammy if she went to prison.

"I can't believe this shit! How the fuck do I get arrested for disorderly conduct when I was the one who got jumped. Somebody's going to lose their job for my unlawful arrest," Dawn said.

Although her mind was in shambles, Tracy noted that Dawn didn't mention that she was unlawfully arrested also.

"I hate fucking Dave. I can't believe he's fucking that broke bitch! I bet she still live in the hood with her fucking mother."

"Shut up!" Tracy screamed.

Dawn was shocked speechless by Tracy's outburst.

"I'm tired of hearing you scream about Dave, your petty ass arrest for disorderly conduct, and who Dave is fucking! I don't care! I have an assault on a police officer! Do you know what that means?"

"Yes. I'm an attorney and I understand the magnitude of your charges...this is all some bullshit. When I get my call, I'm going to call Douglas to straighten this shit out, don't worry."

"Who the fuck is Douglas?"

"Mr. Hall."

Tracy looked at Dawn strangely. As if she was supposed to know that Mr. Hall's first name was Douglas.

"I thought you heard me refer to Mr. Hall by his first name before. Anyway, he's going to chew these cops' asses out."

"Dawn, please just be quiet, my head is killing me."

Dawn sat on the bench across from Tracy and did as Tracy had asked.

A few hours later, the officer opened the cell door and told Dawn that she was free to leave. Tracy looked alarmed as she asked, "What about me?"

The cop just shrugged his shoulders while Tracy continued to spit out questions concerning her release.

"Don't worry, I'm on top of things," Dawn said before she left.

Alone in the holding cell, Tracy stood looking around in disbelief that she was reliving the same nightmare as when she was arrested for assault against Joann.

The next morning, Tracy learned that her bail would be $200,000 and she would need to pay the 10 percent—twenty thousand. Aside from that, when Tracy was told that she was being transferred to the county jail, she vomited, squeamish with fear

· · ·

After her release on her own recognizance, Dawn called Dave. When she got his voicemail, she left her second message of the night: she was locked up and needed for him to come to the police station.

As she sat on the bench watching the door for Dave, she felt guilty for lying to Tracy about calling Mr. Hall. But Dawn had her reasons.

When she was given a call by the police officer, she was too embarrassed to tell Mr. Hall that she had been arrested for rolling around in the streets fighting. So she called Dave instead. Dawn didn't need Dave's legal assistance. She called him, hoping that he felt sympathy for her and blamed himself for her arrest.

· · ·

Sam was furious when she got the call from Tracy stating that she and Dawn were arrested and that she needed twenty thousand dollars to get out. Tracy also informed Sam that Dawn had gotten out and was going to give Mr. Hall a call to get on the case.

When Sam hung up from Tracy, she grunted loudly in frustration, then she wondered why Dawn hadn't called her yet.

...

Dawn entered her apartment at 6:00 a.m. Before she could remove her clothes, her phone rang. She smiled, believing it was Dave. But her smile melted when she looked at the phone and saw Sam's number. She cursed before she answered the call.

Excitedly, Sam told Dawn that Tracy needed twenty thousand. Dawn wasn't shocked. In fact, she expected the bail to be higher. Dawn told Sam she was going to take a shower, and then she was going to go speak with Mr. Hall about the situation. When Sam inquired about raising Tracy's bail money, Dawn rushed off the phone.

As Dawn basked in a hot bubble bath, she blamed Tracy for getting them both in trouble. Dawn thought about the money she was saving for her new home. She had eighteen thousand and decided that she would lend Tracy a least five thousand, nothing more.

As Dawn struggled with the guilt of not offering to pay the whole bail, she justified her position by blaming Tracy for her own predicament for hitting the cop. Lost on Dawn was the fact that she precipitated the fight by challenging the women after Tracy had quelled the argument by apologizing to the women for Dawn's behavior.

...

Tracy was transported to the women's county jail where they house women. After twelve torpid hours at the Police Administrative Building she had nothing to eat but a cheese sandwich, which was washed down with a pint of milk.

FRIENDS

The strip-search she was forced to undergo was a thousand times more degrading than anything she had done while performing on the stage at the strip club.

When Tracy was issued a baggy prison jumpsuit, she stared at it for a moment, wondering how many women had their funky ass in the jumpsuit. Being forced to wear the hand-me-down triggered thoughts of Joann in her negligee.

Once Tracy completed the formalities of her introduction to the "County" she was taken to the cellblock where she was to remain housed until she made bail or was released by the court.

Upon her arrival to the "Block" the first thing she noticed was the noise coming from several different conversations going on simultaneously. Tracy wanted to yell *shut the fuck up* to the yapping women, but fear caused her to remain silent.

Although she was new to the jail experience, settling in was the furthest thing from her mind. Tracy wanted and needed to use the phone. As she headed for the telephone, she recalled the warning by a woman who had been transported along with her to the county. The woman told her that most of the trouble at the jail was because of the telephones. In no time, Tracy would learn how true the woman's words were.

Within ten minutes of moving to the block, she got into a fist fight with a woman looking for trouble.

While Tracy was waiting to use the phone, she was standing behind a woman on the phone arguing with her boyfriend. Tracy had overheard the woman begging the boyfriend not to leave her. Just as Tracy smirked, the woman turned around and saw her.

When the phone time expired, the woman asked Tracy what was so funny. When Tracy opened her mouth to say nothing, the woman put her fist in it. A fight ensued and Tracy was jumped by the woman and two of her cronies.

That night, Tracy sat on the dirty cell floor in the "Hole"—solitary confinement. She had bruised ribs from the women stomping her, and even worse, her left eye was swelled and had turned black.

Shrouded in gloom, Tracy did what weakened souls had done in her situation, she thought of young Dorothy from the Wizard of Oz. As Tracy's mind teased her, suggesting that she was in a dream, Tracy closed her eyes and tapped her heels together three times while uttering, "I want to go home."

But unlike Dorothy, Tracy wasn't wearing special shoes, nor did she get Dorothy's saying correct, which was, "There's no place like home." So when Tracy opened her eyes, she was assured something that she had known all along: she wasn't in a dream, and the closest thing to a wicked witch was the woman who had punched her in the mouth and blacked her eye.

Once again, forced to deal with reality, Tracy crawled in bed, wishing she was never born.

. . .

Dawn entered the law firm an hour later than her usual early-bird arrival. Even though her tardiness wasn't an issue, she felt weird for altering her daily routine.

Once she settled into her office, she immediately checked her messages, which were none. She took a few sips from her morning cup of black decaffeinated coffee, no cream or sugar, and prepared herself to approach Mr. Hall to reveal that she had been arrested. She dreaded what she was facing, but it was something that had to be done since he would find out for himself sooner or later.

As she stood in front of her desk preening her clothes, she mumbled her practiced speech and headed for Mr. Hall's office. She knocked twice, then entered the posh office.

Mr. Hall, who was on the phone, gave her a smile and motioned for her to have a seat. When Dawn remained standing and looking uneasy, Mr. Hall told the caller that he had to go and he hung up the phone.

"Dawn, what is it?"

Dawn closed her eyes, fluttering her eyebrows, "I don't know how to tell you this...but I know you're going to be disappointed in me."

Mr. Hall's face grew more vexed by the second. He walked around the desk over to Dawn, taking her hands in his own. Standing before her, he looked more like a father rather than a lover as he told Dawn, "Sweetheart, you can tell me anything."

"I was arrested last night," Dawn said with her voice wavering.

Mr. Hall scowled, causing his brow to wrinkle. Dawn couldn't determine if he was angry, disappointed, or both. Dawn walked away, taking a seat on the couch and cupping her face in her hands while tears spilled from her eyes. Mr. Hall paused for a moment, and then he sat next to her while placing a consoling arm around her shoulders.

His quick wit told him that her arrest couldn't have been anything serious or she would still be in jail and calling him for assistance. He pulled out a handkerchief and dabbed the tears from her face.

"Don't cry, sweetheart, what did you get arrested for?"

"Disorderly conduct."

Mr. Hall chuckled and squeezed Dawn's shoulder playfully. She was surprised by his relaxed reaction. Although she believed that the disclosure of her arrest to Mr. Hall would come as a bombshell, to her relief, it was nothing more than a dud firecracker.

"That's it? Disorderly conduct."

"Yes."

"What's the big deal? You're in my camp. We're not your run-of-the-mill law firm. I can make something like that disappear, don't you know that?"

Dawn shook her head "yes." She gazed at him with watery eyes filled with appreciation and admiration. She felt honored to be the mistress of one who she believed to be a powerful man.

"Now, tell me what went down, from beginning to end."

Dawn remembered the advice that Mr. Hall had once gave her that whenever she had to speak on the matter of law, envision that she was speaking to a jury of twelve to save her client's life. So Dawn stood up, held her head high, and paced the floor as she began to convey the details of the incident that led to her arrest.

Conveniently, Dawn decided to begin the story after she threw the bottle at Dave's car.

"My friend...Tracy and I were walking to our car, minding our own business. We were accosted by two hood-rats who had too much firewater in their system. Well, one of the women called me a bitch. I ignored her. But these bitches were relentless in their verbal assault. Next thing I know, I'm on the ground being jumped. Tracy comes to my aide, somehow the police showed up, Tracy hits a cop, now she's in jail, I was released on R.O.R."

Mr. Hall stood up and rubbed his chin, apparently in deep thought. Dawn watched him in silence. The longer she studied him, the more gigantic in her eyes he became.

"Is this Tracy a personal friend?"

The pointed question caught Dawn by surprise. For starters, she didn't know where Mr. Hall was heading. It was common practice that a lawyer never asked a question without knowing the possible responses the question might get. Secondly, she had to seriously ask herself did she consider Tracy a true friend.

"Yes, she is my friend," Dawn said with certainty.

"Is this the same friend you represented in another case?"

"Yes."

"Will you be representing her again?"

"Well, I don't know?"

"How is her financial situation, can she afford counsel?"

"She's broke. She didn't mean to hit the cop. In fact, she didn't see the cop behind her."

Mr. Hall folded his hands and looked down at the floor. Dawn wondered what was going on in his mind. She didn't have to wait long to find out.

"I will do everything legally possible on your friend's behalf."

In a reactionary moment, Dawn rushed to Mr. Hall, hugging him and kissed him on the mouth. When their tongues touched, she slowly disengaged.

They both stood in stone silence, avoiding eye contact. This was the first time they had ever kissed on the mouth. The other kisses before were to her cheek or forehead.

The buoyant atmosphere in the room seemed to slowly fade. It was as if she had crossed a sacred line. Mr. Hall considered tongue kisses and intercourse solely for his wife. Although he felt displeased by the kiss, he didn't convey his feeling to Dawn.

For her part, Dawn was repulsed by the kiss. She thought Mr. Hall's tongue tasted like skim milk. It left an unflattering taste in her own mouth. She wanted to brush her teeth. But like Mr. Hall, Dawn kept her feeling to herself.

"I just was overly excited."

"I understand...your friend should be in the county by now. I'll get over there today or tomorrow to interview her."

"Thank you."

"I would do anything for you, sweetheart, you know that."

Dawn smiled warmly at Mr. Hall before walking back to her office and sitting at her desk. She thought about the kiss and how horrible it was.

The infamous kiss—and Mr. Hall's rigid reaction to it—changed something in Dawn, igniting her spontaneous nature. At that instant, the attraction she had for Mr. Hall flew out the window. She folded her hands on the desk and wondered how and when she was going to end their relationship.

Dawn figured the breakup would have to be done in a way not to provoke a vendetta. She decided that the best way to achieve her goal was to somehow leave enough clues for Mrs. Hall to discover the affair. What became of Mr. Hall's marriage wasn't a concern of Dawn's. Her only interest was to end the affair and, hopefully, remain cordial with Mr. Hall in case she needed him in the future.

Developing a headache from plotting and scheming, Dawn closed her eyes, inhaled slowly, held her breath a moment, and then released it. She repeated the stress relieving technique several times before making up her mind that once Tracy's case was adjudicated, she would commence with the breakup.

Later that afternoon, Sam stormed into Dawn's office. Although Dawn was expecting her, Dawn wasn't expecting the rude entrance.

"Tracy is in the fucking hole!"

"What?"

"Yeah, I went to visit her and they told me I couldn't see her because she was in the hole for fighting."

"Tracy has to control her temper."

"How do you know she started the trouble?" Sam retorted.

Dawn saw the look on Sam's face and thought it wise not to get into an argument at that time.

"You're right, Sam."

"What are we going to do about her bail? I have three thousand. How much do you have?"

"Five thousand."

"Five stacks? Come on, Dawn, I know you have more than five stacks. What about the money for your house? How much did you tell me you had saved up?"

While Sam frowned trying to remember the exact amount Dawn had mentioned having, Dawn wished she had never revealed to her friends that she was saving for the single-family home that cost in the area of six figures.

"I told you how much I have, five, that's it. I just gave the realtor a considerable amount of money last week."

Dawn lied with a straight face and an even voice. Usually, Sam could detect when Dawn was lying, but today she couldn't, so she decided to appeal to Dawn's guilt in an effort to sniff out the truth.

"Your friend is sitting in jail and you have the means to help but you won't."

"How dare you come in here and accuse me of not helping. I got Douglas to represent Tracy. Do you know his hourly rates? Plus, I'm putting up my hard earned money for her bail. I resent you for accusing me of being less of a friend."

Being put in her place, Sam was gripped with silence.

"I just can't believe this shit is happening again. She just got off of one case. Now this."

"Calm down, Sam, I'm frustrated as well."

"Tammy had been asking for her. I hate lying to a child...so we got eight thousand, and I don't know where to get the rest of the money...if we don't raise her bail money, she will have to sit in the county until trial."

"Why don't you put up your house for collateral?"

That was an idea Sam hadn't thought about.

"I don't know. I could talk to Andrew."

"Well, do that. Right now, I have work to do. Give me a call later."

Sam turned to leave and stopped at the door. With a stone-face and the belief that Dawn wasn't forthcoming with the amount of money she had, Sam turned back to Dawn and said, "In times like this, friendship needs to be tested. Isn't that what you always say?"

Before Dawn could respond, Sam left. Dawn slammed her palm down angrily on the desk, "Don't question my friendship!"

...

It was midday, two weeks after her arrest, Tracy lay curled up on her bunk, sobbing in despair. Besides the official legal visit from Mr. Hall, which was encouraging, and the letter she received from Sam, Tracy had no other contact with anyone else on the outside.

Even though Sam had mentioned that she would put up her house as collateral, Tracy couldn't shake the funk she was in. The isolation was taking its toll, slowly stripping away any morsel of hope she had managed to harbor.

An hour later, the guard yelled into Tracy's cell that she had made bail. She initially thought it was a dream, but within seconds, she hopped off the bed ready to taste freedom.

When Tracy exited the jail, Sam and Dawn were waiting for her. As Tracy crossed the streets hurrying over to her friends, they were shocked to see the deteriorating effects from her two weeks of incarceration.

Tracy's weight loss was noticeable, even behind her loose-fitting dress. Her face looked gaunt and two years older. Her hair was kinky and dirty because she only showered twice. Tracy did, however, wash a few times at the sink.

Sam stepped forward and embraced Tracy tightly. The two women held each other like they hadn't seen each other in years. Wrapped in Sam's comforting enfold, Tracy felt loved; it was something she needed after her ghastly stint in jail.

"It's going to be okay, Tracy," Sam said softly.

Dawn moved to embrace Tracy, but her efforts were halted when Tracy snapped, "Why the fuck did you start that fight?"

Blindsided by Tracy's sudden outburst, Dawn was shaken and at a loss for words. Even Sam was caught off guard.

Ignoring Dawn, Tracy directed to Sam, "How is Tammy?"

"She's misses you, but otherwise, she's fine."

"Douglas said your case --" Dawn said.

"I don't want to talk about that right now! I just want to get my daughter and go home and take a bath...I have to pick up my car, too."

Dawn and Sam exchanged a look that didn't sit well with Tracy.

"What's going on?"

"Your car is gone," Sam said.

"No! Stolen, repossessed?"

Sam shrugged her shoulders while Dawn remained silent. Overcome with disappointment, Tracy placed her hand on her forehead and turned in a circle, laughing nervously. Sam thought Tracy was about to lose it.

"What else? What else, Sam…Dawn? When I go home is my house going to be there? I bet I don't have a job. How am I going to buy food? I should go back to jail, at least they'll feed me."

Dawn looked unsympathetic as she folded her arms across her chest and watched Tracy. But Sam knew Tracy needed affection, so she placed her arms around friend's shoulder.

"Let's just get out of here?" said Sam.

"I'm going to meet y'all later. I have to make a stop," Dawn said.

Without waiting for a response, Dawn walked to her car while Sam and Tracy hopped in Sam's car. Once at Sam's house, Tracy thanked Andrew for his support and then left with Sam and Tammy.

Sam pulled her car to the curb in front of Tracy's house. Before she exited the car, Tracy told Sam that she owed her. Sam waved her off replying, "This is what friends do."

When Tracy entered her house, she kneeled down and picked up her mail, and of course they were credit card bills and two shut-off notices. She tossed the envelopes on the table and took a seat on the sofa. She felt good to be in the comfort of her own home.

Just as she was about to stand and head upstairs to take a hot bath, Tammy asked, "Mommy, did you learn a lot in school?"

"What?"

"Did you learn a lot in school? Aunt Sam said I had to stay with them because you were at school."

Overwhelmed with emotions, Tracy's tears cascaded down her cheeks as she just stared at Tammy, who began to cry herself. She wanted to tell her daughter the truth, but how could she tell the child she wasn't in school, but in jail.

There was nothing Tracy could say or do but call Tammy over to her. She took the child in her lap and cradled her until they both fell asleep.

...

Although she didn't show it at the time, Dawn was livid when Tracy had shouted in her face about starting the fight with the two women that night outside of the club.

A half-hour later when Dawn stepped out the elevator to her law firm, she was still peeved over Tracy's outburst. At that point, Dawn made up her mind that she wasn't going to allow Tracy, or anyone else for that matter, to hold her responsible for Tracy getting locked up. *You hit the cop, not me,* Dawn thought as she headed to her office.

As Dawn passed the receptionist seated at her desk, the receptionist said hello and gave Dawn an extended smile. *Why was she so chipper?* crossed Dawn's mind as she looked back at the receptionist, who was still smiling at her.

The next peculiar moment was when a paralegal winked at her as they walked by each other in the hallway. Dawn stopped and placed her hands on her hips, wondering what was going on with these people who never displayed this sort of behavior towards her.

The moment Dawn entered her office and saw the bouquet of assorted flowers on her desk, she understood why everyone was behaving so chummy towards her. She placed her hand over her mouth while her eyes exhibited her surprise.

"Who sent these?" she asked herself.

This was Dawn's first time getting a gift of flowers. Before today, she thought it was corny for men to send a woman flowers. She only felt like that because no one had ever showered upon her romantic gifts or flowers. But now that she was the recipient of such, she had a change of heart as she was swept away with delight.

Dawn rushed over to the flowers and sniffed them, enjoying their earthly sweet fragrance. She removed the card with a message on it: I think of you always.

Curiosity tickled her emotions as Dawn smiled, wondering who could've sent the flowers. Her first thought was that it was a beautiful attempt by Dave to apologize for the scene he caused the other night at the club. She picked up the phone and called him. This was their first communication since the club.

In a sexy voice, Dawn said, "Hi David, I got the flowers. They are so beautiful. I mean -- thank you so much!"

As she listened to Dave's response, her joyous expression withered away. Upset, she hung up the phone feeling like a fool. Dave had told her that he didn't send the flowers and would be pleased if she forgot his phone number.

Her next speculation was with certainty that it was Mr. Hall, because there were no other men in her life. She didn't think enough of herself as having the physical attractiveness to catch the eye of a secret admirer.

Right before she was about to rush to his office, Mr. Hall entered. He, too, displayed an overly friendly smile, resembling the one worn by the paralegal and the receptionist.

Dawn stood next to the flowers, folded her arms across her chest, and flashed a perky smile, waiting for him to fess up to being the sender.

"Hello, Dawn...I see someone sent you flowers."

Dawn unfolded her arms and slowly lost her smile while studying his face for some hint that his statement was a joke.

"You're joking right? You didn't send them?"

"No...I'm sure there's a card with them."

"Yes."

Dawn handed the card to Mr. Hall. He read the card and then handed it back to her. Mr. Hall gave Dawn a disfavorable look, and without saying a word, he left the office.

Dawn was not moved by his behavior. *Fuck his attitude. Shit, he has a wife and that's why I'm ending this relationship.* She wanted to march into his office and scream her sentiments in his face.

Perplexed, Dawn sat down and re-read the card. Afterwards, she called the flower store. The only information the clerk at the store could provide was that the sender was a man.

Dawn hung up the phone and paced the room, wondering who sent the flowers; was it someone from her past trying to ease their way back into her life now that she was on the verge of being successful? After juggling a few names and faces in her mind, she still didn't have a clue, so she decided to stop stressing about the matter. Like most things of this nature, Dawn knew that sooner or later the admirer would reveal himself.

When Dawn left work and approached her car, she saw a greeting card under the windshield wiper. She looked around to see if someone was watching her, but the area was deserted.

As she sat in her car reading the greeting card, she hoped that the flowers and the card weren't a sick joke, or sent by a deranged stalker who meant her no good.

• • •

Tracy awoke refreshed from a much needed goodnight sleep. She lay in bed appreciating the softness of her sheets and blanket. It had been two weeks since she was able to sleep through the night without awaking several times to the harsh reminder that she was in jail.

Though it was difficult, Tracy crawled out of her warm bed, slugging her way into the bathroom. After using the toilet, she turned on both faucets to the bathtub. When she thought the water was warmed up enough, she placed her hand under the water and then snatched it back from the coldness. She turned off the cold water, leaving the hot water running. Once again, she placed her hand under the spigot and felt cold water.

"Damn, they shut it off!"

Tracy turned off the faucet, stood erect, looked up at the ceiling, and sighed heavily out of frustration. Her world was crumbling and there was nothing she could do to reverse it.

Breakfast for Tracy and Tammy was cereal and milk. It was okay with Tammy, who was like most children in her situation, oblivious that the world around her was falling apart.

Following breakfast, Tracy and Tammy left the house and stopped at the corner grocery store. It was owned by a fifty-something married couple.

The husband was a handsome man who was a real hound. He went after every twenty and thirty-something cutie that stepped foot in his establishment. Most of the women brushed him off as a horny old man.

When Tracy and Tammy entered the store, it was empty, besides the owner. He was standing behind the counter. When he saw Tracy, his eyes lit up with delight. Tracy saw his reaction and ignored it like she had done numerous times before.

After picking up a couple of items, Tracy brought them to the counter.

"How are my two favorite women?"

"Hi, Mr. Charlie," Tracy said politely.

Taking his time to bag Tracy's items, the owner said, "I haven't seen you in awhile. I thought you moved."

"No, I was just away."

"She was at school," Tammy blurted out.

Although she was caught off guard by the remark, Tracy didn't show it. The owner raised a questioning eyebrow. He had no clue what the child was talking about, nor did he care, and Tracy didn't bother to elaborate.

After paying her tab and retrieving the bag—while being careful not to touch the owner's hand as he always hoped—Tracy and Tammy headed towards the door. Upon reaching the door, the owner hurried from around the counter and opened the door for Tracy.

"Thank you," said Tracy.

"When are you going to let me take your sexy self out to dinner?" the owner whispered into Tracy's ear.

Any other day, Tracy would've responded by saying something sarcastic: will your wife be joining us? Or sometimes Tracy would outright ignore the comment. But today she paused. The owner was surprised. He was expecting the usual sarcastic response. He licked his lips smiling, thinking that he had finally broken down her wall.

"Just come back tonight right before I close." Again, he whispered out of earshot of Tammy.

Tracy's heart was racing. She just looked at the owner with a serious face and left. The owner watched her through the window. He prayed that she would take him up on his invitation.

While thinking about the store owner's invitation, Tracy glanced at her watch. In a force of habit, she looked up the block for her parked car, forgetting that it had been repossessed.

Later that afternoon, Tracy dropped Tammy off at Sam's house and then took public transportation to her job, or rather, the place where she used to work. Tracy had called the manager earlier and was told to pick up her check because her employment was terminated due to absences.

After picking up her check, which was a drop in the bucket compared to the finances needed to pay her debts, Tracy stopped in a couple of shops, inquiring if they were hiring. Unfortunately, nothing was available.

Dejected, but not broken, Tracy returned home. She picked up the phone to call Sam and ask if Tammy could stay the night. She discovered that the phone had been disconnected. In frustration, she hurled the cordless phone across the room.

Smoldering with anger, Tracy wanted to hit something or someone. She started talking to herself; she was asking questions about what she did wrong in life to receive this steady flow of setbacks, one after the other.

Suddenly, she stopped the sinful questioning. With a determined look, she marched up to her bathroom. With cold water, she washed her face, underneath her arms, and between her legs. Once in her bedroom, she changed into a skintight dress, sprayed perfume on, and strolled out of the house, headed to the corner store.

Halfway to the store, she saw the owner locking up for the evening. She took a quick survey of the block. Satisfied that no one was outside, she eased up behind the owner and said, "Damn, you're closed."

The owner recognized the voice and turned around with a smile.

"Girl, you know I would keep this store open all night for you."

"Never mind," Tracy said.

As Tracy turned, pretending to leave, the owner placed his hand on her shoulder. Tracy's eyes darted about, checking for watching neighbors. She was thankful no one had witnessed the interaction.

Later that evening in the apartment above the corner store, Tracy dressed quickly while the owner lay in bed watching her. Although she felt a sense of guilt for her actions, she had to admit the sex was surprisingly good.

"I'm sorry about your situation. You should've been hollering at me. I want you to know this wasn't about money. I like you and that little girl and want to look out for y'all. You understand what I'm telling you?"

Tracy nodded her head "yes."

"Don't mention this to nobody. I don't want people in my business," the owner said.

Like I'm going to tell someone I tricked for a couple of dollars.

"When you need something, you come to me...Okay?"

"Alright."

"You know I have a wife."

"Yes."

The man stood up, slipped on his pants, then walked over to Tracy and kissed her on the lips.

"Let me walk you down to the door."

The owner stood in the doorway of the side door, watching for traffic and neighbors. When the coast was clear, he mentioned that it was okay for Tracy to leave. As she walked by him, he smacked her on her ass. His new ass. The one he claimed for himself.

Later that night, Tracy lay alone in bed. Although her eyes were closed, she was unable to sleep. Over and over again, she tried to justify that sleeping with the store owner was for more than the three hundred dollars he gave her.

She told herself, since he had been flirting with her for years, they just finally hooked up and he looked out because she was in trouble.

But no matter how she tried to spin the situation, she had to face the reality that she had just fucked for a buck.

So she resigned to the fact that she had found herself a "sugar daddy" that she was going to milk like a cow.

CHAPTER

8

The courtroom was buzzing with activity; several defendants that were shackled together sat nervously, waiting to go before the judge to be arraigned for minor offenses. Dawn, who was clad in an expensive pantsuit, was bent slightly in front of the defense table, shuffling legal papers.

In the back of the gallery sat A'Man. He was watching Dawn. She was now standing next to her client while she addressed the court.

Dawn had no idea that she was being closely watched by A'Man, nor did she know that he was in the courtroom. Furthermore, she didn't even realize that she was on his radar.

As A'Man studied Dawn's unassuming shape from behind, he wondered what it was about this woman that had him thinking about her ever since the first time he met her at the law firm. *Was it because she had rebuffed my advances that day at the law firm? Or was it her profession that made her appealing? It certainly wasn't the looks, they were less than average.* Whatever it was, A'Man was eager to find out.

After his failed cognition of why he wanted Dawn, A'Man slipped out of the courtroom and decided to wait for her out in the hallway.

Ten minutes later, at the moment A'Man turned his head to look at something that had gotten his attention, Dawn exited the courtroom, flanked by her client. She was so engaged in her conversation that she didn't notice A'Man when she walked by him.

If A'Man hadn't turned back when he did, he would've missed Dawn, who was now a few feet away from him. Before Dawn was too far away, A'Man called out to her.

"Miss Counselor!"

Dawn stopped, turned around, and saw A'Man smiling back at her. She whispered something to her client. He shook her hand, and then he walked away. As A'Man strolled up to her, Dawn tried not to be too obvious as she checked him out.

"Hello, Dawn."

"Hi. A'Man, right?"

"Yeah."

"What are you doing here? You have another case? Where is Mr. Hall, is he close by?" said Dawn, looking around.

"No...I don't have any business with the court. Thank God."

"Then why are you here?"

Dawn looked confused. A'Man stood silent for a moment, just checking her out to the point where she felt embarrassed.

"Did you win your case?" A'Man asked, redirecting the conversation.

"I just had to make an appearance."

"It's about lunch time, can I buy you something to eat?"

Dawn was surprised by the invitation. A'Man could see that she was contemplating a decision. Her eyes said yes off the bat, but there were other factors to consider: Why was A'Man here in the first place? For a second, she thought Mr. Hall might even be testing her.

"So?"

"Did you come here today looking for me?"

"Yes."

Another surprise—Dawn was suspicious. She looked A'Man over, noting that with his good looks he could probably get any woman he wanted. *Why me?*

"Did you send me flowers?"

"Did you like them and the card I left on your car?"

"They were a pleasant surprise," Dawn said, thinking, *this is weird.*

A'Man picked up on Dawn's apprehensions and chuckled.

"Yo," I'm not a stalker or a woman-killer. Even since I first saw you, I wanted to talk to you again. Then I saw you when I was with Mr. Hall, so I had to wait. The other day I was walking by a flower store and thought it would be a nice touch to send you flowers. Don't you think you deserve flowers every now and then?"

Dawn felt flattered. She wanted to scream to the clouds, *Yes! Yes!* But she held her composure.

"What did you want to talk to me about?"

" You "

"I like the flowers, the compliment, but I don't date clients of the firm."

"I'm no longer represented by your firm."

"Or former clients."

"I didn't say anything about dating or you being my woman. I just asked could I take you to lunch."

Dawn hesitated a moment, then said, "Okay."

In a small restaurant with a plate of salad in front of her, Dawn sat across the table from A'Man, who had a burger and fries.

Because A'Man was staring in her eyes, Dawn felt bashful and couldn't eat.

"Why are you looking at me like that?" Dawn asked.

"Like what?"

"I don't know. Like you are...with your eyes."

A'Man chuckled softly. *This will be easy. I won't have to swing my bat to score.*

Dawn asked herself in silence, *what does this guy want with me?*

In a surprise move, A'Man reached across the table and picked up Dawn's idle fork. He stuck the fork in Dawn's salad and raised the fork to her mouth. Dawn hesitated a minute. Then she ate the food from the fork while looking into A'Man's eyes.

"It's good?" asked A'Man.

Dawn was simply blown away. She couldn't stop staring into his eyes. Those hypnotizing eyes that were igniting something in her. She was determined to fight whatever it was that was happening to her. She kept thinking, ethics over passion.

Just when A'Man was about to hit her with another move, Dawn stood up, thanked him for the lunch, and made her way out of the restaurant without looking back. A'Man sat at the table befuddled.

Twenty minutes later, Dawn entered her office. She stood in front of the window, looking out. Thoughts were swirling in her mind. She didn't run away from A'Man out of dislike for him. She knew if she had stayed in his company, she would've probably wound up in his bed, or he in hers.

As she sat engulfed in thoughts of A'Man, Mr. Hall entered quietly as he was accustomed to doing. When he eased up behind Dawn and placed his hands upon her shoulders, surprising her, she jumped and pushed his hands away. Mr. Hall was shocked by her reaction.

"What's your problem?" Mr. Hall asked harshly.

"You scared me! You always scare me when you do that. I don't like to be scared."

Mr. Hall looked at Dawn leerily. This was the first time she had spoken to him in this fashion. He attributed it to one of two things: he did actually scare her, or she was secretly involved with the person who had sent the flowers.

"I didn't mean to snap on you. I was deep in thought."

"Hopefully, your thoughts were auspiciously about me and no one else."

"Actually, it was about a client. She had a tough case."

"Speaking of clients, your friend's preliminary hearing is in a couple of days. I want you to sit in as co-counsel. Hopefully, we can get the case thrown out at that time, but we'll see what happens...we're still on for tonight, aren't we?"

Dawn pondered for a moment before saying, "Sure."

When Mr. Hall left her office, Dawn thought for the first time about moving into her own private practice.

CHAPTER
9

It was a pleasant Sunday afternoon. Rather than take advantage of the warm weather outside, Tracy, Sam, and Dawn chose to chill out at Dawn's apartment and do some catching up. While the women relaxed in the living room, Tammy and Sam's children played in the guest room.

"Your preliminary hearing is scheduled for next week. I will be co-counsel, and I'm sure we'll be able to get the case thrown out. Just like I did with your last case," Dawn said confidently.

While Dawn blabbed on about the legalities of the charges against Tracy, Sam, and Tracy exchanged a look, rolled their eyes, and sighed loudly until Dawn got the message to shut up or change the conversation. When Dawn didn't take the hint, Tracy intervened.

"I have a sponsor," Tracy said proudly.

"Who?" Dawn asked.

"Mr. Charlie, he's like fifty-something."

"You're fucking someone that old? How did that happen?" asked Sam.

"I took off my dress and he went down on me."

While Sam thought Tracy's revelation was amusing, Dawn was silently thinking about her affair with Mr. Hall and whether she should come clean about her own older lover.

"I can't believe you're fucking somebody old enough to be your father," said Sam, shaking her head.

"So what? He's taking care of my bills, plus, he makes me feel good."

"You can't talk, Sam. You were sneaking around with my uncle when you were seventeen and he was thirty," Dawn said defensively.

Tracy heard the defensiveness in Dawn's voice and chalked it up to Dawn needing to challenge Sam's point of view on nearly every topic.

"Andrew and I were different, we were in love and eventually married."

"Y'all weren't married then, and you were underage."

As the women continued to discuss Tracy's newfound lover, Dawn felt that it was a good time to tell the girls about her relationship with Mr. Hall.

"I'm having an affair with Douglas!" Dawn blurted out.

A fog of silence seized the room. Dawn looked at the two stunned faces before her. *What did I do?*

Dawn presumed that Sam and Tracy were judging her harshly in their minds, but actually they were just at a loss for words from shock.

"Well," said Sam matter of factly.

"Well, what?" Dawn asked.

"No wonder you was so guarded about Tracy fucking grandpa. Yeah, I peeped how defensive you were…"

The mood was slowly changing. Tracy sensed that a typical argument was surfacing.

Sam continues, "…but the real question is, can Mr. Hall's old ass fuck?"

Tracy and Dawn burst into loud laughter. The children in the other room came to the door, checking on the commotion.

"Close that door back," Dawn yelled.

"How old is his ass anyway?" Sam asked.

"He's sixty-three or four."

CHARLIE BASSETT JR.

"I knew something was up," Tracy said.

"No you didn't...dude is a cold freak. He likes for me to talk smut over the phone. The other night I was in Dave's hallway, waiting for him to come home. Mr. Hall called, and next thing you know, I'm asking him if he had his dick in his hands!"

The women erupted into laughter.

"Can his old ass get hard...yeah, they take Viagra," Sam said.

"I never had sex with him. All he wants to do is eat me out..."

"That's what my old-head prefers to do!" Tracy said.

"...and I give him hand-jobs, that's it."

"Stop lying, you fucked him," said Sam.

"I swear to God. This guy is a freak. Not only does he want me to jerk him off, I have to punch him on his chest with my other hand."

Once again, Sam and Tracy exploded in laughter as they fell to the sofa in tears. Again, the children opened the door to be nosy, and they got the same response, Dawn shouted at them to close the door.

"I knew those old white men were freaks!" Sam said, still laughing.

After gathering themselves, Sam and Tracy sat up on the sofa while Dawn finished telling them about the affair and her intentions on breaking it off after Tracy's case was over.

Since her two friends were coming clean about their secret affairs, Sam thought it was a good time to drop her bombshell about her one night stand with A'Man, leaving out catching an STD. Sam's only reservation was the blood-relationship between Andrew and Dawn. Sam wasn't sure if the girl-talk would stay with the girls.

Just when Sam made up her mind to reveal her tale, Tracy's cell phone rang. Tracy smiled as she looked at the number on her phone.

"That's my sponsor," said Tracy.

Dawn and Sam looked on while Tracy leaned back on the sofa and talked in a sexy voice into the phone. Several times during the conversation, she winked her eye at her friends.

Suddenly, Sam had a change of heart about disclosing her one-night stand with A'Man. She figured, one day in an angry fit, Dawn might reveal the secret to Andrew.

"Okay, daddy, me too," Tracy said before she hung up.

"Daddy? Me, too? Are you in love?" Dawn asked.

"I didn't say 'me, too' because he said that he loves me. He said he couldn't wait to see me tonight. And I said 'me, too' and stop ear hustling my conversations."

"You're in my house."

"Sam, can you watch Tammy for me tonight?"

"Your so-called daddy better start giving you money for a babysitter."

"Every dime I get goes to my bills. I just had to get my phone and gas turned back on."

As Tracy continued talking about her financial woes, she didn't pay attention to the astonished look on Dawn and Sam's faces. They didn't know that her circumstances were that dire. Dawn realized that Tracy was sleeping with the older man solely for his money.

Although Dawn was doing the same thing, in a sense, with Mr. Hall, she viewed Tracy as a whore. She felt, both, sorrow and disgust for her friend.

"I'm going to speak with Mr. Hall about trying to get you something at the office, Tracy. I'm not making any promises," Dawn said.

Both Tracy and Sam were surprised by the gesture. Sam assumed Dawn had a motive, but she couldn't put her finger on it. Tracy simply thought their afternoon of bonding inspirited Dawn to reach out to her. Tracy walked over and embraced Dawn.

"Thank you."

"Again, I'm not making any promises."

"It's the thought that counts...well, I have a date with Mr. Charlie."

"Stop calling him mister. You should never call the man you're fucking mister...whatever his name is."

Tracy paused and looked to be in deep thought. To everyone's surprise, she said, "Y'all know what...I'm going to call him back and cancel. I'm going to break off the relationship. I like him and everything, but I just don't feel right."

"I feel you," Sam said.

"Don't break off shit, ride this train to the end of the stop," Dawn said.

"You're just saying that because you're dealing with a married man," Sam said.

"No, it's more than that. Life ain't pretty, and sometimes you have to do the hard things to get by."

Dawn had selfish reasons for suggesting that Tracy continue with her adulterous relationship. It was sad, but the lower Tracy appeared in Dawn's eyes, the better Dawn felt about her own self. Although she had a strange love for her friends, her resentment toward them was just as equal, if not more. Dawn remembered well the days when the three of them were together at a club or shopping and two men approached. Dawn was always the one who was ignored, and even when Sam declared that she was married, still, the guys would look past her.

"Go with your first instincts, Tracy," Sam advised.

"No, go with your needs."

"Well, I have a date tonight."

"Y'all bitches are crazy, fucking these grandfathers."

"If you wasn't married --" Dawn said.

"Well, I am, so don't go there...Dawn, I know this is some weird shit, but you should tape that shit with you punching Mr. Hall on his chest. I could make a lot of money selling that CD," Sam said.

"Girl, you're crazy," Dawn said.

"My guy is married," Tracy said.

"He's married?" Sam asked surprisingly.

"Yeah, he's the dude who has the store at the corner of my block."

"Ooooh, Tracy, that's too close for comfort. I don't like that," Sam said.

"I have things covered. Listen, I don't want to talk about that. Sam, you ready?"

"Alright, Dawn, I'll call you later," said Sam.

"Make it tomorrow, I told you I have a date."

"You're going to fuck around and give that man a heart attack one day," Sam said jokingly.

"It would be his fault. Nobody told him to have a fetish for getting beat up while he's coming, fucking freak."

After the children were gathered, the girls exchanged goodbyes.

. . .

At the approach of nightfall, the girls were getting ready for a night of fun and sex with their lovers. First up to swing the bat was Tracy. After freshening up and changing into a mini-dress—bought the previous day by the store owner—she checked herself in the mirror. Satisfied that she was hot enough to start a fire, she exited her house and sashayed towards the store's front apartment.

Although she was looking straight ahead while she walked, her eyes were carefully scanning the block and neighbor's windows, making sure no one was watching.

But just when she was about to make the turn to the side door of the store, she saw someone she knew turn the corner, so she kept walking.

Tracy circled the block. When she approached the store again and believed there were no lookers, she slipped in the side door. Little did she know, the nosiest woman on the block just happened to be looking out of her window at the moment Tracy had stepped to the door. If Tracy hadn't taken one last look back, the woman wouldn't have seen and recognized her face.

The nosy woman, who couldn't be paid to keep a secret, picked up her phone to blab to neighbors about what she had just witnessed.

Minutes later, Tracy lay back with her eyes closed and her body squirming from the pure pleasure and sensation of the store owner's tongue, making her feel like a fulfilled woman.

Tracy moaned. *It doesn't get any better than this.* With each lick of his tongue, each slow stroke, each soft kiss to her cheek, neck, and breast, Tracy's passion for the store owner swelled. She knew she was falling ten thousand feet without a parachute, and it felt good to be floating on air.

But like anyone who jumps intentionally from a plane, after gliding with the wind, there comes a time when the jumper must descend. Tracy's descent was quickly approaching, and being unequipped with a parachute, she was certain to have a crash landing.

After their lovemaking, the store owner handed Tracy a few bills. "Just a little something for you and the baby," as he had put it. Tracy clenched the money in her hand and wrapped her arms around her lover for a goodnight kiss.

Slowly, they made their way down the stairs, fondling each other like teenagers. The owner opened the door and peeped outside. The block was dark and quiet. Nothing was stirring, walking about, or watching, save the unseen nosy woman peering from her upstairs window and waiting.

As Tracy walked out the door all smiles, she never saw the store owner's wife with the stick in her hand. She smacked Tracy on her forehead, causing a deep open wound. Tracy fell to the ground, dazed and bleeding.

"Bitch! You're fucking my husband!'

As the woman continued to wield away, with the stick in hand, the store owner raced out of the building and received the same treatment as Tracy. Fortunately for him, his whack to the head was less damaging than what Tracy had received.

"Aaaaah!" he yelled.

As the husband and wife fought like two men—the husband getting the worse of it—Tracy staggered to her feet with her head bleeding profusely. Neighbors began to spill out of their homes and peer out their windows to watch the ruckus.

"Why are you fucking these little bitches? I'm tired of you embarrassing me!"

Feeling woozy, Tracy collapsed. Finally, neighbors broke up the fight, but no one could silence the wife, who was yelling that Tracy shouldn't have fucked her husband. Being the focus of all the onlookers, Tracy was embarrassed, but she was too dizzy to just walk away.

The police arrived promptly as Tracy was being helped to her feet. Adding to her embarrassment was the sight of Tammy's father, Steve, hurrying towards her. At first, Tracy thought she was hallucinating, until he asked if she was okay.

Steve had come to Tracy's house, trying to persuade her to allow him to spend an hour or so with Tammy. As he knocked on her door, he noticed a crowd of people gathered at the corner. He walked to the commotion for a closer look and saw Tracy sitting on the ground holding her head.

Steve offered to take Tracy to the hospital, but the police intervened and placed Tracy in the patrol car and rushed her to the emergency room.

. . .

In the darkness of Dawn's bedroom, the smooth sounds of jazz drifted from the speakers, setting the mood for lovemaking. Mr. Hall lay in the bed naked; leaning over him was Dawn, who was clad in a sexy Victoria Secret negligee.

Tipsy from the alcohol she consumed with Mr. Hall during the evening, Dawn masturbated him slow and carefully, just how he liked. Mr. Hall let out a heavy and hard moan from the sensation of her gentle hand.

"Oh, baby, that feels fantastic, Dawn."

As Dawn continued her hand motion, she began to punch Mr. Hall in his chest at five-second intervals. The increase of her hand motion was in tune with the increase of Mr. Hall's moaning, heart rate, and erratic breathing.

"Dawn, Dawn! Oh, Dawn!"

Dawn responded by pulling on him harder and faster. Her punches were no longer at five-second intervals, but almost instantaneous. Blinded by the darkness of the room, she couldn't see that pain had replaced pleasure on Mr. Hall's face.

She couldn't see the squeezing or burning pain in the center of his chest, nor could she distinguish his shortness of breath from his erratic breathing. Lost on her was the fact that his sweating was no longer out of pleasure from her gentle repeated strokes, but a symptom of a heart attack.

Like a California earthquake, Mr. Hall's heart attack hit him suddenly. He let out a grunt, not a moan. Dawn picked up on the change of sound. Immediately, she sensed that something was wrong.

She hopped off of the bed, turned on the light, and was horrified at the miserable sight of Mr. Hall. In her shock, Dawn knew that he was suffering a heart attack. For a moment, she froze in fear until a more frightening possibility hit her, Mr. Hall could die in her bed. Dawn rushed to the phone and dialed 911, then she placed another call to a partner in the law firm while telling Mr. Hall that help was on the way.

After she was done talking to the partner, she called Tracy, only to get her voicemail. Frantically, she called Sam and was thankful that Sam answered. Within seconds of their conversation, Dawn heard the sound of approaching sirens. She dropped the phone and ran outside, waving her hands over her head wildly to get the paramedics attention.

As the paramedics attended to Mr. Hall, they exchanged a nervous look. Dawn placed her hand over her mouth and sobbed as she prayed that he didn't die.

...

Sam put the children to bed early. Thereafter, she walked into the bathroom, stripped naked, put on Andrew's robe, and slipped her feet into a pair of heels.

Andrew was lying on the bed, goggling at his beautiful wife as she strutted into the room. Sam clicked on the CD player to some up-tempo, instrumental music. She stepped up on the bed, standing over Andrew with him between her legs. Andrew looked up under the robe and grinned like a junior high school boy catching a revealing shot of his hot teacher.

Moving her body to the rhythm of the music, Sam danced for a moment. Then she seductively undid the robe, letting it fall on Andrew's smiling face.

As the CD changed to a slower pace of music, so did Sam's hips as she gyrated to the sounds. With the fire of passion reaching its boiling point, Andrew pulled Sam down to him.

Sam straddled Andrew, moving slowly to meet his movement. She leaned forward and wrapped her arms around his neck as their lovemaking continued. Although passion filled her mind, somehow her thoughts wandered to why she didn't tell Tracy and Dawn about A'Man. Now she was thinking about A'Man and couldn't get his face out of her mind.

Upset with herself for allowing another man to enter her mind while having sex with her husband, Sam quickened her pace. Andrew matched her speed. The intensity of the sex swiftly chased A'Man out of her mind.

All of a sudden, they switched positions. As Andrew did her from behind, he smacked her ass. Sam moaned. He smacked her on the butt again. The smacking on the butt reminded Sam of her sex with A'Man; he was the first to give her a spanking.

While the spanking and the moaning persisted, Sam slipped and moaned, "A'Man."

Andrew stopped instantly, not sure what he had heard. He asked, "What did you say?"

Sam, thinking fast, remained cool.

"Why did you stop, Andrew? It felt good."

"What did you moan?"

"I said, oh man."

To Sam's relief, Andrew bought the lie. As they continued, Sam had to focus on not having any more slipups.

It was while cuddling in Andrew's arms, winding down from their steamy intercourse, when Sam had received Dawn's call. Dawn was sobbing and saying that she gave Mr. Hall a heart attack. Sam hoped out the bed, dressed quickly, and headed to the hospital closest to where Dawn lived.

. . .

In the hospital's waiting room, Dawn met a woman who just so happened to need an attorney for a lawsuit against a major company. Although she was distraught, Dawn couldn't turn down the prospect of a major payday. Dawn gave the woman her card and borrowed a cigarette.

After the woman left, Dawn lit the cigarette. It was her first smoke in five years. Slowly, she began to pace the room nervously, blaming herself for Mr. Hall's heart attack.

While she was wallowing in self-condemnation, Dawn didn't notice Sam rushing into the room until she screamed Dawn's name. They raced to each other's embrace. Clutching her friend's arm, the tears spilled down Dawn's cheek.

"I killed him! I know I did!"

"They said he was dead?"

"No, but you didn't see him. He looked almost gray, his eyes --"

Dawn couldn't finish as she sat down. Sam sat next to her, rubbing her back consolingly.

"He's going to pull through. Have faith."

When Steve entered the room and saw Sam and Dawn, he assumed they were there for Tracy. Dawn thought that Sam had got in touch with Tracy, and that Tracy had gotten Steve to bring her to the hospital.

"How did y'all hear?" Steve asked.

They both looked at him in shock.

"What are you doing here, Steve?" Sam asked.

"For Tracy. Isn't that why y'all are here?"

Both Dawn and Sam stood abruptly with terrified faces, expecting to hear that Tracy had been in a life threatening accident.

"What happened to Tracy?" Dawn asked.

"She was in a fight. Her head was bleeding, so they brought her here."

"Fighting who?" Sam asked.

"All I know is this old lady was screaming about Tracy fucking her husband. The old lady even beat the dude up."

Sam and Dawn exchanged a look that Steve caught. From their looks, Steve knew that they were privy to Tracy's obvious affair with the older man.

"I don't care what Tracy does, but when it affects my daughter's life --"

"Where were you when Tracy was struggling to feed her daughter? You haven't did shit! When was the last time you dropped some money on her? Now you're trying to judge my girl. Fuck you, punk!" Sam screamed.

"I didn't come here to argue."

"Well, shut the fuck up!" Sam said.

As Sam spew out venomous words, threats, and accusations at Steve—who was taking it all in silence—Mrs. Hall and the partner that Dawn called entered.

Mrs. Hall rushed over to Dawn and embraced her. Sam saw the awkward look on Dawn's face as she hugged the woman back.

"Oh, Dawn, how is he?" Mrs. Hall said through sobs.

"I don't know."

"Thanks for calling, Dawn," the partner said.

"Well, how did it happen? I mean, what happened?" Mrs. Hall asked.

As Dawn struggled for the perfect lie, the doctor entered the room. Mrs. Hall was the first to rush over to him.

"Are you treating my husband, Douglas Hall?"

"Yes...he's in surgery --"

On that, Mrs. Hall fainted. Dawn put her hand over her mouth and sat down, thinking she could have two deaths on her hands. While the doctor tended to Mrs. Hall, Sam's cell phone rang. She answered the call. It was Tracy, who was calling from outside the hospital after receiving fifteen stitches to her forehead.

"That was Tracy, she's outside the hospital," Sam said to Dawn.

"You go ahead, I'm going to stay here."

"Okay, I'll call you later."

After embracing Dawn, Sam left, followed by Steve. Mrs. Hall was wheelchaired to a room for a thorough examination, Dawn was left in the room with the partner.

"I hope they're going to be okay," said the partner, shaking his head.

"Yeah."

"Dawn, the doctor said he might be in surgery for 24 to 30 hours. You get out of here. I'll give you a call if there's an update. There's nothing you can do here."

Dawn thought about it and said, "You're right."

Dawn embraced the partner and left. Later, as she lay in bed, she felt like the rottenest person on earth.

• • •

Tracy stood in front of the mirror in her bedroom, staring at the stitches on her forehead. Once again, another relationship ended in a fight, but this time she had only herself to blame. She thought about Dawn and how they both bragged about sleeping with their older men.

She was about to call Dawn but decided not to, suspecting that Dawn was probably feeling worse than she felt and didn't want to talk. So Tracy climbed in bed and wondered when will her misfortune end.

...

With only three hours of sleep under her belt, Dawn climbed out of bed. She sat on the edge of the bed, debating whether to go to the hospital or to the office. She called the partner for an update of Mr. Hall's surgery. He told her that there was no word yet and that Mrs. Hall was doing better.

Dawn hung up the phone, deciding that she would go to work. Thereafter, she would stop by the hospital, which was only five minutes away from the law firm.

When Dawn arrived at work, she was dressed nicely in a pantsuit, but from lack of sleep and frail nerves, she looked like she had spent the entire night getting knocked around in bumper cars at a carnival.

The law firm was humming with chatter that Dawn and Mr. Hall were together last night when he had his heart attack. However, the chatter wasn't speculative of any hanky-panky between the two; in fact, people were congratulating Dawn for her quick response to the situation.

After she answered a bombardment of questions, Dawn retired to her office. She placed another call to the partner at the hospital. This time the partner conveyed that Mr. Hall was recovering from a successful surgery. Dawn hung up, feeling the weight of an elephant removed from her shoulders.

Dawn closed her eyes and recalled the moment Mrs. Hall had fainted. *How could I continue to hurt that beautiful woman?*

As Dawn contemplated her future, she made up her mind that once Mr. Hall was up and about, she was definitely going to tell him that life is too short and precious to hurt the people you love, so she no longer wanted to hurt Mrs. Hall.

Interrupting Dawn's thoughts was the ringing of her cell phone. She answered and it was the woman she met at the hospital the previous night. As Dawn listened to the woman relate her case, Dawn thought that if she won that lawsuit, the settlement would be more than enough money to start her private practice without starting off as an ambulance chaser or relying on court appointed cases.

As Dawn paced the floor holding her hands behind her back, her thoughts moved to Tracy's case and the possibility that with Mr. Hall out of commission she would have to handle the case alone. This presented another problem. How could she represent Tracy if she could possibly have to be a witness for her? And even if Tracy got another attorney and called her as a witness, Dawn's testimony couldn't help Tracy because she was on the ground getting her ass kicked and didn't see the altercation between Tracy and the cop. More importantly, Dawn wasn't going to lie under oath for no one. So the matter was decided, she could only be helpful as an attorney.

Several hours passed as Dawn was held up in her office forming a strategy for Tracy's defense, when someone knocked on the door. Dawn opened the door and was surprised when she was presented with a bouquet of roses. She smiled like a school girl as she accepted the roses and closed the door. This time, there were no doubts in her mind who was the sender. She sat down and looked at the card with the message: just thinking of you.

Dawn wanted to thank A'Man for the flowers and was a little angry that she didn't have his information. Suddenly, she hurried across the hall to Mr. Hall's office. She snatched open the file cabinet, thumped through a series of files, and smiled when she removed A'Man's divorce folder, jotted down his information on a notepad, and hurried back to her office.

She picked up the phone to call A'Man, then, she paused. She was having second thoughts about crossing the line with a former client. As she dialed his number, she told herself that it was only a thank-you call. But in her heart, she knew that the ethical line she had held in high regard was becoming more blurred by the second.

"Hello?" A'Man answered.

Damn, he sounds good over the phone.

"Hello, hi...this is Dawn."

"I know. I recognize your voice…"

Dawn paused for a moment, wondering if his statement was a lie.

"…I'm not going to ask how did you get my phone number."

"Well, I'm a resourceful woman."

"That's good to know. Are you at work?"

"Yes."

"Do you like the flowers?"

"Of course, but I may begin to get spoiled if you continue behaving in this manner."

As Dawn continued to slyly flirt, the door to her office burst open. In came Mrs. Hall. Her eyes were bloodshot and watery, and looked like she had added ten years to her already sixty-plus years of age."

"I have to call you back."

Dawn hung up the phone and stood up, bracing for bad news.

"What happened with Douglas?" Dawn asked frighteningly.

"How could you? You came to my home, ate my food! I trusted you. I embraced you last night at the hospital like a friend!"

Dawn's face was a mixture of sadness and guilt. *How did she find out?* Mrs. Hall walked up to her. As Dawn, who was short herself, looked down at the petite woman who was a few inches shorter, Dawn searched for apologetic words, but nothing came to mind but the simplest contrived words.

"I'm sorry…I never meant to hurt you."

"Douglas told me everything! You are a whore!"

As Mrs. Hall screamed obscenities at Dawn, a couple of people gathered at the door and watched the confrontation.

"Don't come to the hospital, you're not welcome!"

Mrs. Hall slapped Dawn across the face. Dawn had to struggle hard to hold back her defensive reflexes, but she did. After a few more choice words, Mrs. Hall marched out of the office. The spectators at the door stood there a moment, shaking their heads disappointedly at Dawn. She rushed to the door and slammed it in their judgmental faces. Dawn picked up a cardboard record box and slammed the box down on the desk. She removed a stack of files from the box and started packing her belongings into the box.

. . .

Tracy was goofing around in her living room when Sam entered. Tammy ran over to Sam and jumped into her arms.

"Aunt Sam!"

"Hey, Tammy. How's my little diva?"

"Fine. My mother fell because she was running, now she got fifteen stitches."

Sam chuckled lightly. She placed Tammy on the floor and sat across from Tracy.

"Oh, you fell down?"

"I did fall down," said Tracy in her regular voice. Then she whispered, "Well, I did fall after I got hit with a stick."

"Did you talk to Dawn today?" Sam asked.

"No. I called, but she didn't answer."

"I talked to her? Yeah, we had an interesting conversation. She told me that Mr. Hall was recovering from surgery and that Mrs. Hall stopped by the office, oh, just to slap her."

"What?"

"Yeah, she said old girl found out."

"Damn. Welcome to the club."

"I told y'all both to stop messing around with old men who just happen to have a crazy wife at home."

That brought a giggle from Tracy.

"Dawn also said she packed her shit and left the firm."

Tracy stopped abruptly, "You're kidding me."

"Nope."

Tracy flopped down on the couch and threw up her hands in exasperation. While she considered whether to have Dawn represent her or just go pack her and Tammy's clothes and go on the run, the doorbell rang. Sam held up her hand, gesturing for Tracy to sit tight, and Sam answered the door.

"Tracy, come over here."

Tracy walked to the door and was in shock to see the store owner standing on the steps. Sam stood next to Tracy while she spoke.

"What are you doing here?" Tracy asked annoyingly.

"I want to make sure you're okay."

"Listen, I'm done, okay."

"Just like that?"

"Yes. You're married and I got enough drama in my life."

Tracy started closing the door, but the store owner reached out and held it, preventing her from shutting it closed. His gesture was not in a threatening manner, he just wanted to be heard.

"I said I was done, move your hand."

"Just hear me out."

Sam stepped in front of Tracy and shouted, "Motherfucker, didn't she tell you that she was done? Step the fuck off! Bounce!"

The store owner looked at Tracy's face, which looked in agreement with Sam's sentiments. He let go of the door and strolled away. Sam shut the door.

"You have to be firm with these guys. Some of them just don't get it."

When the women sat back down, Tracy wondered how Sam could be so strong with Mr. Charlie, a stranger; on the other hand, when it came to Andrew and his abuse, she was like a scared, trembling puppy.

"What are you thinking about, Tracy?"

"Tammy."

Upon hearing her name, Tammy climbed on Tracy's lap. At the tender age of four, Tammy looked at her mother's face and could tell that something was bothering her.

"Mommy, what's wrong?"

"Nothing...Tammy, do you know who Steve is?"

"My daddy."

The question caught Sam off guard as she shot Tracy a questioning look, wondering where Tracy was heading.

"Do you want to see him?"

Tammy, who was aware of the rift between her parents, paused for a moment; then she looked to Sam and back to Tracy, wondering what answer her mother was expecting.

"Do you want to see him, Tammy?"

"Yes," Tammy uttered softly.

Tammy hoped she had responded the way her mother had wanted. But Tracy wasn't sure how she felt about Tammy's answer. Tracy looked over at Sam, who shares Tracy's feelings.

"You won't be scared to be alone with him if I'm not there, will you?"

"No. Why should I be scared of my daddy?"

"You shouldn't be scared. He might come over here this weekend to spend some time with you. Is that okay?"

"Yes."

"Do you like going over Aunt Sam's house?"

"Of course she does," Sam said.

"I like it over there," Tammy said gleefully.

"If I have to go away to school, you might have to stay with her until I come home, okay."

"Like before?"

"Something like that...maybe a little longer."

Sam stood up and motioned her head towards the kitchen. Tracy followed her.

"Tracy, you're going to beat those charges."

"What if I don't? I have to prepare Tammy for the possibility of being away from me."

"What about DHS?"

"I don't know. I have a feeling that I'm going to jail. That's how things happen for me."

FRIENDS

Tracy sat at the table and began sobbing. Sam rubbed her shoulder consolingly.

"No matter what Tracy, you can always count on me."

CHAPTER
10

Four days after she walked audaciously away from the law firm, Dawn found an affordable office space to rent. Without delay, she furnished the office with a computer, legal books, and other legal necessities.

Desperate to establish a reputable name for her law office, Dawn reluctantly hired Traćy as a receptionist and placed ads in print and on the internet for a paralegal.

While Dawn stood in front of the bookshelf flipping through the pages of a law book, she glanced at Tracy, who was sitting at her desk reading the newspaper. With the feeling that she was being watched, Tracy looked up from the paper just in time to catch Dawn looking at her before Dawn turned away.

"Why are you staring at me, Dawn?"

"I wasn't staring, I just glanced at you...don't you think it's ironic that last week at my apartment I told you that I would speak to Mr. Hall about finding you something at the law firm, and now you work for me?"

Although Tracy smiled, she wasn't pleased with Dawn's statement. Tracy detected from the tone of Dawn's voice that it was something disingenuous in the way Dawn said, "Now you work for me."

Ticked off by Dawn's self-assertion, Tracy was on the verge of reminding her of two things: first, she had a good job until she lost it when she did Dawn the favor of taking her to get an abortion. Secondly, she was asked by Dawn to be her receptionist. But not wanting to screw things up with her new employment, Tracy held her tongue and was thankful that she was making an honest dollar.

"Are you ready for my preliminary hearing?'

"Absolutely, I'm sure I'll get the case thrown out. Then we can go about the business of getting my practice off the ground --"

"Yeah, we're going to get our law firm rolling," Tracy chimed in.

Dawn stared at Tracy for a moment thinking, my law firm. With that, Dawn walked into her office. She took a seat behind the desk and placed a call to A'Man.

"Hello...how are you doing? I'm doing well...yes, I know it's been a few days...but I've been busy. I'm off on my own now...how did you know? If you knew the address, why didn't you stop by...the purpose of this call, A'Man, is to tell you that I really like you, but I can't be in a relationship right now. Maybe when things in my life get situated...I'm sorry...take care, A'Man."

Dawn hung up the phone, she couldn't believe that she pushed a man like A'Man away. But she was on a mission, and looking at Tracy reminded her of the goals she had set for herself when she was in junior high school.

Although he was attractive and had a body like a male model, Dawn felt that having someone like A'Man at this period in her life would hold her back, and the last thing she wanted to be was a procrastinator or failure.

Dawn despised being someone who was easily distracted by a romantic relationship; someone who struggled from job to job and was ill-prepared for the future. Someone who was dragging a kid around and didn't have a trust or college tuition for her child. Someone on the wrong side of the law, or someone who was waiting to be rescued by a big payday from a lawsuit. Someone like Tracy.

Later that evening, and moments before Dawn and Tracy were about to exit the office, Dawn received a delivery of a bouquet of flowers. Dawn took the flowers in stride, only showing a slight smile, while Tracy was surprised.

"Who sent you flowers?"

"Nobody."

"What are you talking about? You're dealing with somebody and didn't tell me."

"I'm not dealing with anyone and I don't want to talk about the flowers. I'm tired and ready to go home and get some rest. If you like the flowers you can have them."

"Don't bite my head off."

Dawn set the flowers on Tracy's desk just to be smart. Tracy didn't find the gesture amusing. She picked the flowers up and took them into Dawn's office. The two women looked at each other with stern faces for a moment, and then they burst into laughter. As they walked out of the building, Tracy continued to press Dawn about the flowers, but Dawn remained tight-lipped about the sender.

. . .

In a quiet restaurant, A'Man sat alone at a table thinking about how Dawn had brushed him to the side. He hoped the flowers he sent would change her mind, although he didn't have much faith that it would.

Besides A'Man believing that Dawn was the kind of woman that would take care of him financially, he finally figured out why he was attracted to her. Aside from the looks department, Dawn reminded A'Man of his ex-wife, Mirrar: the self-confident, arrogant, and a bit bourgeois woman. With those attributes, A'Man wanted to break Dawn just like he had done Mirrar, and it all stemmed from her rejection of him at the law firm. To have her reject him a second time was unacceptable. He was determined to have her answer for her audacity to put him on the backburner.

CHAPTER

11

Tracy and Dawn were in court for Tracy's preliminary hearing. Of course, Sam was sitting in the gallery, watching the proceeding and praying that the case got thrown out.

Tracy's accuser, the determined-looking police woman, was sitting in the witness chair testifying that when she approached the altercation in which Tracy was involved, she announced that she was a police officer and Tracy looked back and saw her uniform and still swung backwards, catching her on the jaw.

The police officer, who was a skillful witness, paused in her testimony. What transpired next was as if the officer had scripted it herself. The officer glanced at Tracy to gauge her reaction to being accused of hitting the officer, Tracy flinched. The judge raised an eyebrow, staring at Tracy as if he could see through her. His stare was intimidating. To some extent, Tracy was slowly beginning to believe that she was guilty of something. She lowered her head, wishing she could disappear.

When it was Dawn's turn to cross-examine the officer, Dawn's textbook methods were a failure. With no contradiction in the officer's version of events, there was little Dawn could do to rattle the officer, who looked hell-bent on seeing that Tracy went to jail.

When the officer concluded her testimony and walked by Tracy and Dawn, the officer whispered, "Don't worry, I will be showing up for court when this case goes to trial."

It was obvious that the officer had a vendetta, but Tracy couldn't put her finger on why the woman was out to get her for such a minor incident.

Unfortunately for Tracy, she didn't remember that ten years earlier she had a run-in with the officer at a night club before the woman became a cop. On that drink-filled-partying night, Tracy had thrown a drink in the woman's face over a guy.

Sadly for Tracy, the woman had never forgotten the embarrassing night when the club patrons, as well as the woman's own friends, laughed at her.

Dawn felt nausea as the district attorney argued to the judge why Tracy's case should go to trial. To make matters worse, the district attorney presented medical records and photos of the officer with a bruise on her face from the slap she received at the hand of Tracy.

Tracy listened in disbelief at the spin-job by the district attorney and how a minor incident that happened in a split-second could turn out to appear so major. With the proceeding tilting heavily in the favor of the prosecution, Dawn, as well as Tracy, wished Mr. Hall was there to save her hide.

When it was certain that her fate was sealed, seeing that the case was no doubtedly going to trail, all Tracy could do was sit back and smile, shaking her head thinking that anything less than this wouldn't possibly happen for her. Sam couldn't take no more. She decided to wait outside, so she stood abruptly and left the courtroom.

After the preliminary hearing was concluded, Tracy's case was held over for trial. Nevertheless, there was a bright spot to the proceeding; over the district attorney's objections, Tracy was allowed to remain free on bond.

Dawn, in her inexperience as an attorney, petitioned the court for a speedy trial, which was granted. In this kind of assault case, it would have been wise to prolong Tracy's case as long as possible. Given the fact that the victim in the case was a cop, and considering the dangerous profession of a police officer, anything could happen that could prevent the officer from coming to court.

Outside the courtroom, Dawn told Tracy and Sam that she had other legal business, and without saying goodbye, she walked away.

During the drive home, Tracy told Sam that when she gets convicted, she didn't know if she would want Tammy to visit her. Normally, Sam would challenge Tracy's pessimistic view, but after what Sam witnessed in court, it was a strong possibility that Tracy would, in fact, be convicted.

In the ladies room at the Criminal Justice Center, Dawn stood in a closed stall crying. If Dawn was asked about her tears, she would claim that they were for Tracy, but they actually weren't. Dawn's pain didn't come from a friend's case going to trial. What hurt Dawn was that she got her butt kick by the district attorney, and it hurt badly. Dawn had a victory dance planned and she was going to treat the girls to lunch.

After a good cry, she dried her tears and vowed that she would never be unprepared for anything again in her life.

Dawn exited the stall and checked herself in the mirror. After pulling herself together, she drove in her car to the hospital with a stern face. It had been over a week since Mr. Hall had suffered the heart attack. Regardless of the warning given by Mrs. Hall to stay away, Dawn desperately needed to see her mentor.

At the hospital, Dawn checked with the nurse to make sure Mrs. Hall wasn't visiting. Dawn was told that the wife had left ten minutes ago.

As Dawn stood outside Mr. Hall's room, it took her a moment to conquer her sudden apprehensiveness about facing him. When she was good, she took a deep breath and eased open the door to peep inside his room. Mr. Hall was lying on his side with his back facing the door. Dawn assumed that he was asleep. As she was about to close the door and leave, Mr. Hall turned over. When their eyes met, Mr. Hall smiled and waved Dawn in.

"Hello, beautiful," Mr. Hall said in an infirm voice.

"Hello, Douglas."

"I was hoping you would come. I didn't think that you would after what I heard about the office incident. I told my wife everything. I just needed to get things off my chest. I didn't know if I was going to make it or what."

"I'm sorry, Douglas."

"What do you have to be sorry about? This is all my doing, I crossed the line."

"It takes two to tango."

"You didn't have to leave the firm."

"Yes, I did."

"Come back."

"It comes a time when the baby bird must leave the nest and spread her wings."

"Not before their wings are strong enough to carry them on their way."

That statement struck a cord with Dawn. She didn't have a cagey response to shoot back at him. As she stood there staring down at Mr. Hall, a tear fell from her eye. It hurt his already fragile heart to have his prodigy and intimate companion standing before him with tears in her eyes. Instantly, he knew it was more than just her leaving the firm. He reached for her hand, she extended it to him. Her softness and warmth was like a jolt of life.

"What's wrong, Dawn?"

"Nothing I can't handle."

"Dawn, this is me."

"My friend, the one who got arrested for the cop."

"She had her preliminary hearing today, and the D.A. kicked my butt. Well, it was not so much the D.A. kicking my ass, but the cop as a witness. This cop, she had no contradictions and I couldn't shake her. It was like she was out to get Tracy. The case got held over for trial."

Mr. Hall sighed heavily and folded his hands on his chest. In a strong voice he said, "That's how it is with cops, they almost always get the benefit of the doubt when they testify...some cases are strong and there's not much a lawyer can do but try to get the best outcome for their client."

"Do you understand what I'm saying?" Mr. Hall asked.

"Yes."

"You would've done better."

"Never again say that a lawyer would've done a better job than you. You are a fine attorney and will get better. I'll make a call to the D.A's office and see what I can do. I think I have one or two favors left down there...also, there are a couple of cases that I think you should take over, I'm sure there won't be any problems with the clients."

Dawn looked appreciative. That powerful image that had attracted her to Mr. Hall was once again present as he spoke.

"Dawn, I'm retired, and if you ever need me, I'm just a phone call away."

"You take care of yourself."

Dawn kissed Mr. Hall on his cheek and touched the kiss with her palm. Mr. Hall took her hand in his own and held it for a moment, again appreciating her softness. He was going to miss her. They both knew this would be their last touch, so they wanted to savor the moment for as long as they could.

As Dawn drove home, she felt that she had gotten what she had wanted all along from Mr. Hall. She envisioned her future as being bright and prosperous.

...

Ever since her preliminary hearing, Tracy walked around under a cloud of gloom, but the worst was yet to come. As she stood over the sink washing dishes, she looked down at Tammy, who was doing the drying, and figured the time had come for her daughter to meet her father.

CHARLIE BASSETT JR.

An hour later, Steve and Tammy sat on the sofa under the watchful eye of Tracy. Tracy was amazed at Steve and Tammy's interaction. It was like they had spent their entire lives together.

When Steve had gotten the call from Tracy asking if he could stop by the house to officially meet Tammy, he was ecstatic.

Steve's long awaited moment of spending time with his child had finally come to fruition, and he took full advantage of it. Occasionally, he would glance over at Tracy as she displayed a smile, but he could see sadness in her eyes. If you scaled back Tracy's beautiful façade, one could see that she had the sad look of a single mother who had been through the ringer. It was at that moment, Steve felt the guilt of being an absentee father.

Watching Tammy tell Steve about her dolls, friends, and how her mother had fell and got stitches almost brought a tear to Tracy's eye. She wondered how life would've been if she had never broke up with Steve for denying Tammy.

Surprisingly, she pondered the prospect of going back to him. Even more surprisingly, while Tracy was daydreaming, Tammy had fallen asleep, resting her head on Steve's lap.

Tracy walked over in front of Steve and glanced at her watch, indicating that it was time to wrap things up. Steve carefully laid Tammy on the sofa without awaking her. Tracy walked to the front door and Steve reluctantly followed her.

"Thank you for letting me see Tammy."

"You're welcome. I can't believe how she took to you."

"She's my blood."

Tracy had to catch herself from responding with a sarcastic remark. She was thinking that blood doesn't buy food or clothing.

"We'll make arrangements for you to see her more often. We don't need those people in our business."

"No doubt."

"How are you doing?" Steve asked, touching Tracy's cheek softly.

"I'm maintaining, but things are hard."

Steve handed Tracy two-hundred dollars.

"I'll give you something else this weekend. I'm going to start playing my part."

"We'll see."

"I will," Steve said defensively.

"I'm not trying to start an argument, I'm just saying we'll see."

"Are you with someone?'

"No, I'm concentrating on me and my daughter."

"That's what's up."

As they stood awkwardly looking at each other, it was obvious that both of them were entertaining the same thoughts. Steve wanted to spend some more time at the house and see where things went from there. Tracy was craving a good fuck to knock off some tension, and she was debating whether to let Steve be the one.

"What are you about to get into tonight?" Steve asked with a smile.

Tracy returned the smile, but before she could answer, her cell phone rang. For a second, she started to let the call go to voicemail, but she changed her mind and answered.

"Hello…hey, Sam."

Hearing that it was Sam and not a man gave credence to Steve's hope that he might get lucky on this night.

"Oh, you're at the movies…no, it went good…she liked him…" said Tracy looking at Steve.

He smiled back at Tracy and winked his eye.

"…she fell asleep on his lap…no, he's still here…no…I said I wasn't…okay, bye."

Tracy hung up the phone as she walked back over to Steve. He could see from the look on her face that she had a change of heart about letting him stay. Steve wanted to curse Sam out for cock-blocking.

"Well, I'm going to take Tammy upstairs."

Steve looked disappointed as he said, "I was trying to stay awhile."

"Steve, I'll see you later. I mean some other time."

"Alright," said Steve as he sighed.

Steve kissed Tracy on her cheek and left. Tracy sat on the sofa and chuckled lightly as she thought about what would've happened if Sam didn't call.

• • •

Meanwhile, it was a family night out for Sam and her family; they decided to catch a movie. While Andrew and the children were watching the movie, Sam went to the bathroom and placed a call to Tracy.

After warning Tracy not to sleep with Steve, Sam stopped at the concession stand and ordered buttered popcorn. As she waited, a soft hand touched her face gently. Sam smiled, assuming it was Andrew checking on her for being away too long.

Sam turned around smiling until she saw A'Man. Her smile was replaced by the shock on her face. She dropped the popcorn and shoved A'Man violently.

"Don't fucking touch me!" Sam yelled.

A'Man was taken aback by her reaction. He thought it was a bit overboard.

"Damn, I'm sorry, Sam."

"You don't know me! Don't be saying my name."

"Why are you tripping?"

"You don't know me!"

"Alright then," said A'Man with a chuckle.

Sam rolled her eyes at A'Man, then she hurried to the ladies room.

"Shit! Shit!" Sam uttered.

As terror grasped Sam's being, she wanted to stay in the bathroom until the movies closed and everyone left. Five minutes later, she glanced at her watch and knew that Andrew would come looking for her at any minute, so she exited the bathroom and was thankful that A'Man had gone back to watch the movie or left the theater.

Sam took her seat next to Andrew, who was laughing with the children at the comical scene on the movie screen.

"What took you so long?" Andrew asked.

"I had to throw up."

"What's wrong with you?"

"My stomach," Sam said with a grunt.

Sam held her stomach and leaned forward, pretending that she was about to vomit. Andrew passed her an empty popcorn container and placed his hand on her back.

"We have to go home," Sam said.

The children voiced their disappointments as the family made their way out of the theater. But not before Sam spotted A'Man sitting in the third row from the door with his arms around a cutie. A'Man looked forward, but from the corner of his eye, he saw Sam glance at him.

When the family arrived home, Sam went straight to the bathroom and stayed there for ten minutes, wrestling with whether to tell Andrew about A'Man before the secret came back to bite her.

...

Across town, Dawn stayed late at the office, laboring over legal research. Ever since the preliminary hearing, her practice had picked up considerably. She attributed the work to Mr. Hall.

While her face was glued to the computer monitor, she received a call from Mr. Hall. It was their first communication since the hospital visit.

When he said, "Hello, beautiful," she was all smiles. But her flattered facial expression fainted when he related that he had contacted the D.A's office and was able to get a deal on behalf of Tracy. The original deal offered was two to four years, but Mr. Hall was successful on getting it down to six to twelve months. He insisted that Tracy take the plea.

After exchanging pleasantries, Dawn thanked Mr. Hall and hung up the phone. She thought about Tracy and Tammy, and then she realized that she had to separate herself from being a friend to being an attorney. She called Tracy. When Tracy answered, Dawn said in an authoritative voice, "Hello, Tracy. Let me cut through the small talk. I got you a deal for six to twelve, I suggest you take it."

There was a moment of silence, and then Tracy exhaled heavily. Still, Tracy didn't speak, but Dawn could hear her breathing over the phone.

"I can't do six years for something I didn't do. What about Tammy.

"Months, Tracy. Six months."

Again there was a moment of silence. Dawn assumed Tracy was pondering the deal.

"This cop is out to get you. If we go to trial and lose, you could get a considerable amount of time."

"There is always a chance you can beat the case, right?"

"Yes. I spoke to Douglas and I detailed your case. Your problem is this: it's your word against the cop's. You saw her at the preliminary hearing. Not only is she a cop and her testimony is usually held in high regard as credible, but she's an excellent witness --"

"She was too good."

"I thought long and hard about your case. Most cops wouldn't waste time with a case like this. Are you sure you never had a run-in with this bitch? Did you fuck her boyfriend when you were fifteen? Did you kick her ass during recess?"

"I can't remember this chick. But I feel it's personal."

"What about the deal, Tracy?"

"When do I have to give you an answer?"

"You have two days?"

"That's too soon."

"I'm just the messenger."

"I'll let you know in the morning."

Tracy hung up the phone. She wished that she hadn't allowed Sam to put her house up for bond, otherwise, she would be out of dodge before sunrise.

...

While Sam lay in bed next to Andrew, she made up her mind to tell him about A'Man.

"Andrew, I need to tell you something."

"What?"

Sam hesitated. When she opened her mouth to speak, the phone rang. She answered, it was Tracy. Sam told Tracy to hold on a second.

"We'll talk after I take this call," Sam directed to Andrew.

Tracy related that she was offered a deal for six months and was going to take it if Sam agreed to keep Tammy while she was in jail.

"Of course," Sam said.

Sam hung up the phone. Andrew was staring at her.

"What did you want to say?" Andrew asked.

"Tracy is going to take a deal for six months for the case against the cop, and I offered to take care of Tammy."

"Is that what you wanted to talk about?"

"Yes."

"I don't have a problem with Tammy staying here."

Sam kissed her husband. As Sam made love with her body and spirit, thoughts of A'Man eclipsed her mind. She was convinced that if she didn't talk to someone about her affair with A'Man, she, along with her marriage, would crumble underneath the weight of her secret.

CHAPTER

12

On a sun-filled morning, Tracy stood next to Dawn in a quiet courtroom. As the D.A spoke to the judge, Dawn leaned over and whispered into Tracy's ear, "It's the right thing to do."

After Tracy was questioned as to whether she was knowingly entering into the plea agreement, Dawn extended her pen to Tracy. She hesitated to take it. Skeptical that Tracy might renege on her intentions, Dawn whispered, "It won't be wise to back out now."

Moments later, Tracy took the pen, and with a shaky hand, she signed the plea agreement on the table in front of her.

Thereafter, the judge informed Tracy that she had two weeks to tie up her affairs before she was required to turn herself in at 10:00 a.m. at the Criminal Justice Center.

Following the hearing, Tracy and Dawn exited the building and headed for Dawn's car without exchanging one word to each other. While Dawn walked at a hastened pace, Tracy proceeded slowly through the parking lot.

Suddenly, Tracy was overcome by a compelling need to reflect on her surroundings. She stopped a few feet away from Dawn's car and looked upward. As she gazed at the beautiful sky, she began to think about the things she was going to miss while she was locked up: taking baths and long drives, and smelling and eating good food. Dawn turned and watched Tracy, who was lost in thought.

"What's wrong, Tracy?"

On the brink of having to go to prison, Tracy had an eye opening experience about the reality of the little things around her that are often overlooked and only thought about when they are taken away.

"You know, we take a lot of things for granted. In two weeks, all the things that I never paid attention to before will be lost to me while I'm locked up with those funky bitches."

"It's only for six months."

"One day in prison is too long for a person who doesn't deserve it."

"You're right," said Dawn guiltily.

"Look at that bird, flying like it doesn't have a care in the world."

"Tracy, why are you doing this to yourself? Let's just go back to the office, or I can take you home."

"I don't know," said Tracy woefully. "Take me to the zoo."

Dawn looked at Tracy like she finally went over the edge. But to the contrary, Tracy was more sane, focused, and conscious than she had never been in her life.

"Stop playing," said Dawn smiling.

"I'm serious. Give me a ride to the zoo."

Fulfilling her friend's desires, Dawn drove Tracy to the Philadelphia Zoo. Before Tracy got out of the car, Dawn said, with a bit sarcasm in her condescending voice, "I hope you find what it is you're looking for."

As Tracy stood silently, staring at a lion in its cage, her eyes welled with tears out of sympathy for the imprisoned animal whose eyes looked sadder than her own.

Even though Tracy had brought Tammy to the zoo on a handful of occasions, she never looked at the animals as prisoners, revoked of the freedom to roam wild and free in their natural habitat. Never before today did Tracy view their treatment as cruel and unusual punishment.

As her thoughts switched to her own pending incarceration and the past time she spent in jail, Tracy wondered if the guards looked at her like a zoo specimen while she was locked in her cell. With that notion, she wanted to unlock each cage and free every animal. Then she chuckled while thinking that with her luck, she'd probably be the only person who got mauled or killed by the fleeing animals she liberated.

After leaving the zoo, Tracy caught the bus back to Center City. She stopped in China Town for lunch. While she was in the restaurant enjoying her food, she saw Rob and Joann walking through the door and lost her appetite. As they walked towards her table, she ducked down. When they passed without seeing her, she left her food on the table and walked briskly out of the restaurant, pissed that the cheaters had ruined her lunch.

With the two hundred dollars in her pocketbook that Steve had given her, Tracy walked over to the Gallery Mall to buy something for Tammy. But once at the mall, she decided that since she was going to be in jail, the money would be better served with Sam to help out with Tammy's needs.

As Tracy walked through the mall window-shopping, it occurred to her that she had to call her landlord to inform him that she would be moving because of circumstances beyond her control. She also needed to sell her furniture. Whatever proceeds she received from the furniture, she would, also, give to Sam.

After Tracy was bored with looking at things she couldn't afford, she left the mall. While heading to the subway, her cell phone rang.

"Hello? Hey, Dawn...yes, I'm still in town, but I'm about to catch the sub to Sam's to pick up Tammy...why didn't you do it when we left court? Okay, I'll do it, bye."

Tracy hung up and sighed heavily. Instead of catching the subway-train, she made a detour to a store for Dawn so she could pick up some papers from a client.

A moment after Tracy entered the store, three masked men rushed in brandishing handguns. Before any one of the six or so people there could react, the gunmen were shouting for everyone to lie face down on the floor. Tracy and the other occupants kissed the floor immediately. Helpless, all Tracy could do was shake her head and pray that she made it out alive.

While the assailants proceeded to rob the establishment and each individual, Tracy breathed a sigh of relief when the gunman closest to her bypassed searching her and went on to search someone else. Just when she was convinced that she was in the clear, another gunman hurried over to her.

As the gunman stood over Tracy for a moment, admiring her body from the back, Tracy wondered what the robber was doing. Suddenly, he snatched her pocketbook from her arm. Then in a gruff voice, he ordered her to remove the necklace she was wearing.

Tracy cursed silently. The necklace was a personal gift from a late relative, and it was the only thing of value she actually owned. While her nervous hands fiddled with the necklace lock, the robber checked her pockets, but before he was done, he rubbed his hands between Tracy's legs up to her vagina. Tracy panicked with fear as the pervert's hand molested her. Then as quickly as they came, the robbers left.

It took a moment for Tracy to pull herself up from the floor. Even after the police arrived, she was still visibly shaken and angry. After she had given her statement of the circumstances surrounding the robbery, the police gave Tracy a ride to Dawn's office.

When Tracy walked into the office, her hair was in disarray and her eyes were bloodshot red. Dawn rushed over to Tracy, assuming that she was in a fight.

"Tracy, what happened?"

It took a moment for Tracy to speak, but when she did, it was in a grisly voice, "I hate this fucking city! These fucking people lost their damn minds! Every time I step up to help someone, I get the short end of the stick. I didn't even want to go there! But, me being the friend that I am..."

"What happened?" Dawn shouted.

"The fucking place you sent me to got robbed, and the motherfucker touched me!"

"Who touched you?"

"The fucking perverted robber put his nasty ass hand between my legs! Can you just take me over to Sam's to get Tammy and take us home?"

As Dawn drove Tracy to Sam's, Tracy related the details of the robbery and her humiliation from being fondled. When she asked Dawn how could she defend individuals who would harm another person, steal, or murder someone, a fierce argument ensued. Until finally, Dawn reminded Tracy that everyone is presumed innocent until proven guilty. And sometimes innocent people are still found guilty. That hit home with Tracy, silencing her.

After picking up Tammy and heading to Tracy's house, the sound of approaching sirens caused Dawn to pull to the side to let the roaring fire truck pass.

"I'd bet they're going to my house," said Tracy impassively.

"Don't say that," Dawn said.

When Dawn turned the corner to Tracy's block, the street was blocked by a fire truck. Tracy and Dawn exited the vehicle staring at each other, believing that Tracy's statement might be true.

With her heart racing, Tracy looked down the block and saw that the house ablazed appeared to be her own or the house next door. She knew it was her house. As she ran down the block and saw the smoke pouring out of her windows, her beliefs were confirmed.

A neighbor told Tracy that the fire started after an explosion was heard next door, and the fire department believed that the fire was started by a faulty water heater.

As everyone watched the firemen battle the blaze, several people told Tracy how lucky she was that she wasn't at home when the fire started. Tracy silently disagreed with each of them. She was thinking about the money she lost from the sale of her furniture.

Hours later when the fire was extinguished, Tracy's house was reduced to rubble with nothing left to salvage. Although she wasn't excited about the idea, Dawn offered Tracy and Tammy a room at her apartment.

That night in bed, with Tammy asleep under her arm, Tracy had a twisted thought; she concluded that with everything around her spiraling downward, it might be a good thing to go to jail for awhile and come out with a fresh start.

CHAPTER
13

On the eve of her surrender, Tracy dined with Sam and Dawn at a five-star restaurant. On Tracy's last night of freedom, Dawn suggested that they go clubbing. Taking in consideration Tracy and Dawn's last experience on club night, Sam recommended a quiet dinner for the three of them. Tracy concurred.

"I can't believe you're not going to get any dick tonight. If it was me..." Dawn said.

"That's the last thing on my mind."

"Everything is not about a man, Dawn," Sam said.

"You're right. That's probably why I don't have one."

"No, the reason why you don't have a man is because you put the last one in the hospital with all that pulling and punching on him like you was crazy," Sam joked.

Sam and Tracy burst into laughter as they slapped palms together. Although Dawn thought the statement was funny, she reserved her laughter, due to the serious nature of Mr. Hall's illness.

"That's not funny, the man could've died," said Dawn.

"But he didn't, so don't sweat it," Sam remarked.

"Damn, I'm going to miss y'all," said Tracy with a frown.

"Don't worry, we're going to visit you every week," Sam said assuringly.

"Don't fall in love in there," said Dawn with a smirk.

"It's a women's prison, the only men are guards," Tracy said.

When Tracy finally got the joke, she giggled along with Dawn and Sam and gave Dawn a friendly push.

"I only play on one side of the street."

"Just mind your business and you'll be okay," Dawn said.

"Did you take care of everything you needed to?" Sam asked.

"Yeah. I told Steve that because of the fire, me and Tammy are going out of town for a couple of months to stay with a relative. Of course, he was bitching now that he's trying to play daddy. He wants us to move in with him, imagine that."

"That's something to consider when you get out," said Dawn.

"When I get out...I'm not going backwards on nothing. Now if you don't want us to stay with you until I get on my feet, let me know now."

"Stop tripping." Dawn replied.

"What are you going to tell Steve six months from now when he asks why haven't you called him? You know he's going to be pissed," Sam said.

"Fuck his feelings. For four years he wasn't worried about Tammy, so we're not worried about him."

"I'll be back, I have to use the bathroom," said Dawn, standing.

When Dawn walked away from the table, Sam's expression changed to a more serious look. Tracy took notice and placed a light hand on Sam's shoulder, swaying her.

"Don't look like that, I'm going to be alright."

"I know."

"Well, cheer up. You're not going to start crying and ruin my party."

"Remember when I told you that Andrew had kicked me in the butt?"

"Don't tell me, he's starting his shit again!"

177

"Naw, everything is good. Better than good," said Sam, looking in the direction of the ladies room. "I slept with this guy..."

Tracy looked shocked. She shot a quick look in the direction of the ladies room to make sure Dawn wasn't returning.

"Oh my god, when?"

"It wasn't recently."

"Who was it?"

"Nobody you now. It was the night Andrew kicked me in the ass. I met this guy in the bar. Actually, I met him before. No, twice before I saw him in the bar that night. We started talking...I said fuck it and went home with the dude, now I can't get him out my head."

"Wow," said Tracy softly.

"I don't even like this guy. He looks good and everything. He looks real good. I love my husband. Anyway, the other night I ran into him at the movie. Imagine if Andrew saw him touch my face."

"Why was he touching your face?"

"I was buying popcorn and he came up from behind and rubbed my cheek. I thought it was Andrew. I cursed the guy out and told him that he didn't know me. I hope he got the message."

"You can't trust these dudes. This fool might see you with Andrew and say some dumb shit like, Sam, when are we going to hook up again."

"Andrew would kill him."

"And you."

"I don't want to think about it. Tracy, I got it bad. I'm thinking about this guy all the time, even when I'm with Andrew. The disturbing part is I don't want to sleep with him again. I really don't. I think that holding this secret to myself was wearing me out. Now that I'm actually talking about it, I feel relieved."

"They say that keeping secrets and lies can cause some people to have back trouble."

"Well, I didn't feel it in my back. This motherfucker was in my head...I'm glad I got this off my chest. This shit was killing me, but I feel better now. Don't mention this to Dawn, she can't hold water."

"Yeah, all you need is to get in an argument with her. Next thing you know she's calling Andrew."

"I didn't tell you, but Andrew burned me."

"What?"

"I'll tell you later, here comes Dawn," Sam said quickly.

Dawn walked back to the table and noticed the suspicious looks on the faces of Sam and Tracy.

"What was y'all talking about?"

"Nothing," said Sam.

"Don't tell me nothing. Both of y'all are sitting here looking like y'all got a secret, or were y'all talking about me?"

"I was just asking Sam if she thought that me and Tammy would be stepping on your toes when we move in your apartment when I get out of prison."

"I feel offended."

"I told Tracy that friendship needs to be tested. Isn't that your quote, Dawn?"

"Did I pass the test?" asked Dawn with a confident smile.

"The jury is still out on that one," Sam said.

Dawn didn't like Sam's response, but she let it ride so they could enjoy their night without a fight.

Later that night, Sam made love to Andrew, and for the first time in weeks, she didn't think of no one but the man who was deep inside of her

...

It was a little before 10:00 p.m. when Tracy awoke Tammy from sleep. Once Tammy shook off her grogginess, Tracy instructed the little girl to tell Steve that she was going to miss her father and she couldn't wait to spend some more

179

time with him. Tracy called Steve and told him that Tammy wanted to speak with him before their trip tomorrow morning.

Tracy passed Tammy the phone and listened while Tammy conveyed exactly what she was told to say. When she was finished and Steve said goodbye, Tammy handed the phone back to Tracy.

"Yeah, Steve, I'll call you when we get there. Take care of yourself. Okay, bye."

Tracy hung up the phone and looked at Tammy, who was already back to sleep.

"I'm sorry, Tammy," Tracy said before falling asleep herself.

Across the hall, Dawn moaned as she masturbated. Ten minutes later she put her "little friend" back into the dresser-drawer. *Who needs a man?* The following morning, Tracy awoke with emptiness in her stomach unlike anything she had ever experienced. The hollowness in her gut wasn't from the lack of food; even if she wanted to eat, she couldn't. For this was the day of another depressing chapter in her life.

Just two hours away from turning herself in, Tracy had renewed her thought of waking Tammy and skipping town. As Tracy grappled with the idea of going on the run, a soft knock on the door disturbed her thoughts.

"Tracy, I'm just making sure you're up," said Dawn as she cracked the door open.

After breakfast—a breakfast where Tracy didn't touch her food—Dawn drove Tracy and Tammy over to Sam's house. The gathering was funeral-like with Tracy receiving a hefty dose of encouraging statements, "Keep your head up. The time is going to fly. We're here for you," and the likes.

Tracy's patience was tested as she sat quietly listening to the farewell rhetoric. She didn't want to be rude, but she wanted to scream at everyone to shut up. When it was time to leave, Tracy hugged Tammy tightly. She kissed her daughter repeatedly and said in a broken voice, "I love you more than I love myself. You be a good girl and listen to Aunt Sam and Uncle Andrew. I love you, Tammy."

"I love you too, mommy."

Tracy gave Tammy one last kiss before leaving with Dawn. Twenty minutes later, Dawn and Tracy arrived at the Criminal Justice Center.

"Tracy, don't get in any trouble, but don't take shit off of anyone. I know you don't like when I say it, but those six months are going to fly by. Like I said before, we're going to visit every week."

"Just make sure Tammy's okay."

After tying up her business with the court, Dawn embraced Tracy and walked away quickly. Tracy suspected that Dawn didn't want Tracy to see the tears in her eyes. But Dawn wasn't crying. She had learned to separate friend from client.

Dawn sat behind the wheel of her parked car. She clicked on the CD, and then started the car, and suddenly, Tracy's departure to the slammer hit Dawn. The tears spilled down her cheeks. In the need to cheer herself up, she called A'Man.

Tracy was transported to the county jail. Once she went through the prison reception process, she was escorted along with three other prisoners to the cellblock where she was to be housed.

With her property in hand and a rigid don't-fuck-with-me expression on her face, Tracy's eyes quickly scanned the block, looking for the three women who had jumped her during her first stay. To Tracy's relief, there were no familiar faces.

When Tracy walked into her cell still wearing the stern look, her cellmate was sitting on the bottom bunk reading a magazine. The cute girl, who was around Tracy's age, stood up and extended her hand. Tracy sat her box on the floor and shook the women's hand with a firm grip. The woman, who was no stranger to jail, figured Tracy's toughness was a façade because people who are really tough don't try to show it.

"How are you doing, I'm Monica."

"Tracy."

"I guess you get the top."

Tracy didn't respond. She climbed on her bunk, folded her hands behind her head, and stared at the ceiling.

"Are you okay?" Monica asked.

"Check this out, I'm not trying to be smart, but I don't feel like talking right now."

Understanding the situation, Monica wasn't offended. She sat on her bunk and resumed reading her magazine.

. . .

While a naked Dawn was getting out of bed, A'Man smacked her on the butt.

"Don't be long, baby."

Dawn smiled and walked to the bathroom. She sat on the toilet, smiling as she thought about the sex she had just had, which was far better than with Dave or her late-night liaison with Mr. Hall. She thought A'Man was a keeper if he wanted a commitment.

When Dawn opened the bathroom door to exit, A'Man was standing beside the door, waiting in the nude.

Damn, his body looks ripped. She was suddenly embarrassed to be naked in front of A'Man.

"What took you so long, baby?"

"I wasn't long."

"I can't wait to be inside you again."

Dawn grinned at the prospect while A'Man placed his hands on her hips from behind and walked her back to the bedroom. He pushed Dawn facedown to the bed and climbed on top of her.

CHAPTER

14

It took a few weeks of being quietly reserved until Tracy was finally able to break out of her protective shell and embrace her circumstances. It wasn't that she was afraid of being locked up. She had conquered those fears during her first incarceration. Tracy just wanted to do her six months and put prison behind her.

Tracy was still bunking with Monica, who was the perfect cellmate. She didn't smoke cigarettes or weed and she didn't evade Tracy's space. Although Monica was talkative, when Tracy was going through her period of adjustment, Monica said only what was necessary so not to annoy. An added plus to having Monica as a cellmate was that she had her own and didn't have to beg or borrow anything from Tracy, who was well taken care of, thanks to the money orders from Sam and Dawn.

It was a little after 8:00 a.m. on a Saturday morning, Tracy was sitting on her bunk writing a letter when Monica entered looking excitedly jubilant.

"Hey, cellie," Monica said.

The word "Cellie" was an abridgment for cellmate, a term frequently used by prisoners. Keeping in fashion with the prison lingo, Tracy and Monica often referred to each other as cellie.

"Why are you so happy?" asked Tracy as she closed her notebook.

"I just got off the phone with my man. He's coming up today, so I get to meet your daughter and your girlfriends."

"That's good."

Without warning, Monica began removing her clothes as she talked about taking a shower to get ready for her visit. Tracy was caught off guard and embarrassed.

In prison, it's common knowledge and a respectable practice that before removing one's clothes, a cellmate would tell the other that he or she was about to change or get in the shower, which is the cue that, "I need some privacy."

"Let me get out of here while you do your thing," said Tracy.

"Girl, don't worry about it. I'll only be a second, you don't have to leave."

"No, you need your privacy."

Tracy felt uncomfortable when she hopped off the bunk and caught a glimpse of Monica's breast just as Monica had removed her bra.

"Girl, I can't wait to see my man."

While Tracy sat out in the day-room, she thought about Monica exposing her breast. Tracy debated with herself whether the act was deliberate or spontaneous and whether she should address the issue with Monica or let it be. Factoring in Monica's excitement for her upcoming visit, Tracy decided to let the matter pass.

An hour later when Tracy and Monica were in the cell, the guard shouted that there was a visit. Monica rushed to the door and took the visitor's pass, but she was disappointed that it was for Tracy and not for herself.

"It's for you."

"He'll be up," Tracy said, seeing Monica's disappointment.

"Yeah, I'll see you out there in a minute. My man is just late."

As Tracy sat in the visiting room, she heard Tammy's voice scream, "Mommy!"

FRIENDS

Tammy ran and jumped into Tracy's arm. Tracy kissed Tammy all over her face. Sam walked over and hugged Tracy. After the embrace, Tracy looked towards the entrance expecting to see someone.

"Where's Dawn?"

"She said she'll come up by herself in a couple of days."

"Mommy, how long do you have to stay in school? Because when I go to school, I come home the same day. Why don't you come home after school? I don't know anybody who spends the night at their school."

"This is like a boarding school where the girls have to spend the night."

Although she hated to lie, Tracy looked at it like it was for the greater good.

"How are you doing, Tammy?"

"Fine."

"Sam, tell me about that thing, you know, when you got hot down there…"

Tammy looked at her mother questionably. Being consistently in the company of adults, Tammy learned quickly when adults were engaging in deceptive conversation, and today she was determined to pick up whatever information she could.

Sam said, "I went to see those people, you know the ones we see for the routine…"

"What people?" Tammy asked.

"Let Aunt Sam finish. I get a call telling me I'm like your house."

"How can you be like a house?" Tammy inquired.

Sam and Tracy laughed while Tammy thought about the house burning down, but she couldn't put one and one together that Sam was talking about being burned with a STD.

"So you know I'm flaming. I'm riding around thinking about what to do. I'm ready to tell hubby about everything with the one-nighter, until he tells me that I need to get checked because he's seeing...you can put the rest together."

"Wow."

"Yeah, I was F'ed up."

"You wanted to curse," Tammy said, happy that she finally picked up on something.

"You're right, Aunt Sam wanted to curse. Anyway, that's it."

"You know I'm mad at you, Sam?" said Tracy, smiling.

"Why?"

"All this going on and it takes me to come to ja--I mean school to hear about it."

Tracy was thankful that Tammy didn't question why she changed words in mid-sentence.

"So what do you do in here?"

"I exercise. My roommate is cool, she was supposed to be out here. I guess her boyfriend stood her up."

"Boyfriend," said Sam with a sarcastic chuckle, "Guys don't visit chicks in here. Look around. You don't see no men in here visiting nobody, they're out there doing their thing. You better tell your roommate to wake up."

"That's on her. I'm reading entrepreneur magazines, I'm also reading this novel called *I'll Take Your Man*. It's about this chick named Ashley, she's out of control."

"Didn't you have enough of people messing with somebody else's man?"

"Don't go there. What's up with this guy Dawn's dealing with?"

"I don't know. Since you been here, I've only spoken with her twice. I take it that this guy got her hemmed up."

"Not Dawn, she's too into her career."

• • •

At an expensive men's clothing store, Dawn stood at the counter holding A'Man's hand. As the clerk was processing Dawn's credit card, Dawn felt proud that she was treating A'Man to another outfit, but at the same time, his sly smile didn't sit well with her. She couldn't decipher whether he was appreciative of the gift.

In the following weeks of their first get-together, Dawn and A'Man's relationship had been a whirlwind of sex, shopping, and dinners, with Dawn footing the bills for everything except for the first two dinners of the relationship and the occasional flowers sent to her office.

"What's wrong, baby?" said A'Man, sensing that something was bothering Dawn.

"Nothing, let's get out of here."

While driving A'Man to her apartment, Dawn changed her mind about going home, and she made a turn, heading over to Sam's house. A'Man noticed the change of direction and asked, "I thought we were going to your place?"

"I have to stop at my uncle's house."

• • •

Back at the prison, visiting hours were over. As the visitors filed out, Tammy ran back over to Tracy, who was waving goodbye.

"Mommy, come home with us. You can come back tomorrow."

Tracy was crushed as she fought back tears. She picked Tammy up and hugged her tightly.

"I can't baby, but I'll be home soon."

"No! You don't have to be in school."

"I love you Tammy, but I have to stay."

The guard gave Tracy a look to wrap it up. In turn, Tracy motioned with her eyes for Sam to take Tammy. It took a bit of effort to pry a crying Tammy from her strong grip on her mother's arm.

When Tracy returned to her cell, Monica looked pissed as she lay on her bunk with her arms folded across her chest.

"I hate my boyfriend, with his lying ass. Now I'll be wrong if I started fucking his best friend when I get out."

Tracy didn't respond. She climbed on her bunk and began sobbing. Monica heard the crying and stood up.

"Tracy, are you okay?"

Again, Tracy remained silent as she shifted to her side, facing the wall.

"Is you're little girl okay?"

"She didn't want to leave me."

"I'm sorry. I went through the same thing when I first came here. The only thing I can tell you is try to be strong. I cried for days. I feel so bad. Here I am bitching about this guy who didn't care enough to come see me, and you're going through it about your child. I'm sorry."

"It's not your fault."

It took a trip to Chuck E. Cheese's to finally calm Tammy down from having to leave her mother behind at what she now believed to be a "bad school."

Thereafter, Sam took the smiling four-year-old girl home. When Sam and Tammy entered the house, Sam's youngest daughter scurried over to her and said, "Mommy, cousin Dawn is over here with A'Man."

Naturally, Sam assumed that her daughter was referring to Dawn's new boyfriend and not the infamous A'Man.

"Where are they?"

"In the kitchen with daddy."

"Where is your sister and brother?"

"Upstairs."

"You and Tammy go upstairs with them. I'll be up in a minute."

Curious to meet the man who had swept Dawn off her feet, Sam hurried to the kitchen and stood in the doorway. Dawn was sitting at the table while Andrew was at the far end of the room talking with A'Man, whose back was to Sam. Dawn winked at Sam and motioned her head in the direction of A'Man.

"What's up, baby," Andrew said.

"Hey," responded Sam.

A'Man turned around slowly. When he and Sam laid eyes on each other, they both flinched. Dawn saw Sam's reaction and assumed that Sam was just shocked at how good A'Man looked. Although A'Man himself was surprised to see Sam standing before him, besides his initial reaction, he remained stolid.

Sam, however, was traumatized. Her knees were ready to buckle under the weight of her shock. It took a moment for Sam to compose herself. She prayed that her eyes, which were wide with shock, didn't give her away.

Dawn walked over to A'Man and snuggled under his arm. When he leaned down and kissed Dawn on the top of her head, Sam wanted to vomit.

"A'Man, this is my cousin Sam, my uncle's wife."

A'Man crossed the kitchen over to Sam and extended his hand to her. She paused for a moment, wishing she had an axe to sever his hand at the wrist. Realizing that all eyes were on her, Sam shook his hand with a sweaty palm, giving his hand a little squeeze. A'Man smiled at Sam and overrode her squeeze with a firm grip of his own.

"Pleased to meet you," Sam said in a weak voice.

"How's Tracy?" Dawn asked.

Before Sam responded, she watched A'Man walk back over to Dawn, who happily resumed her position back under his arm.

"She's okay. She wanted to know why you didn't come up."

"Did you tell her what I said."

"Yeah."

"I'll be back in a minute, I have to check on the kids," Andrew said as he was leaving the kitchen.

As Dawn related how she and A'Man met—bragging about the flowers and the greeting card he left under her windshield wiper—Sam sat at the table gawking at A'Man while thinking: this can't be happening. She also wondered why would A'Man court someone like Dawn in such a romantic manner.

"From the first day I saw Dawn I wanted to be with her," A'Man chimed in.

As A'Man continued to profess his affection and caring interest in having a long-term relationship with Dawn, she hung onto his every word. But Sam didn't buy it. The idea of Dawn and A'Man being a couple didn't fix.

"You have to keep an eye on them. Kids are slick," Andrew said, entering the kitchen.

"I want a lot of children running around the house," A'Man directed to Dawn.

Dawn gave Sam a halfhearted smile. Sam knew Dawn had no intentions on having children, at least, in the near future. With the conversation moving into an uncomfortable topic for Dawn, she tapped A'Man on his shoulder.

"Well, baby, you met my family. It's time to get out of here."

"A'Man, give me a call so we can get together this weekend," Andrew said.

"Alright."

A'Man formed a slight grin and glanced at Sam out of the corner of his eye. She began to feel that he was taunting her silently. Sam's intuition was correct.

As A'Man and Dawn walked by Sam, A'Man stopped and turned back to Sam and asked, "Are you okay? You don't look too well."

Sam didn't respond. It took all her restraint not to gash out A'Man's eyes with her fingernails.

Later that evening Sam called Dawn under the guise of talking about Tracy. But Sam's true intentions for the call were to make sure Dawn and A'Man weren't together. Two minutes into the call, Sam asked Dawn was she in for the night. When Dawn responded affirmatively, Sam made an excuse to rush off the phone.

Ten minutes later, Sam was banging on A'Man's front door. Although he grimaced when he snatched open the door and saw Sam, he was actually expecting a visit from her.

"What's wrong with you knocking on my door like you're the police!"

"You think this is a joke?" Sam yelled.

"First of all, stop screaming at me. Secondly, what are you talking about?"

"Don't play games with me!"

"Girl, what are you talking about?"

"You knew Dawn was my friend!"

"How would I know that? I met Dawn at her law firm. One of the lawyers there was representing me on a case."

"I hate you!"

In an unexpected act of rage, Sam grabbed A'Man by the neck. She tried to choke him, but he was too strong. He quickly clenched her wrists and twisted them free of him.

"You better calm down, girl!"

"Fuck you! Why did you come to my house?"

"I didn't know it was your house."

"I'm sure Dawn mentioned my name to you at one time or another. It should've rang a bell!" Sam screamed.

"I'm not going to stand here and argue with you, I have neighbors. If you want to have a civilized conversation, come inside."

Sam scoffed, "You're trying to get me in bed!"

"You lost your mind, I'm closing the door."

"Wait!" In a calm voice, she said, "I don't care what you do with Dawn. What happened between us is dead and I'd like to keep it between the two of us."

"I'm not trying to ruin your family."

"So we have an understanding?"

With a grin, A'Man winked his eye and said, "It's our secret. We're like family now."

"No, we're not! Just stay away from me and my family. I caught that little grin at my house."

"What grin?"

"The same grin you just did. I'm not playing! Don't make me--"

"Don't make you what? Are you threatening me?"

"Try me."

Without further discussion, Sam strode to her car. A'Man slammed his front door. As he thought about the look in Sam's eyes and the implied warning, he recalled the time he had gotten stabbed by a scornful woman who had warned him not to fuck with her. With that in mind, A'Man decided that he better take the warning seriously.

Just as Sam pulled out of her parking spot, Dawn turned onto the block. They missed each other by a matter of seconds.

• • •

It was a little after 4:00 a.m. Tracy and Monica's cell was pitch-black and quiet. Tracy lay awoke on the top bunk, collecting her thoughts. She had her and Tammy's future all planned out; she was going to get her receptionist job back with Dawn and take some night classes. Tracy smiled in the dark. *Just five more months until freedom.*

"Umm," Monica moaned from the bottom bunk.

When Monica slid her hand in her panties, she assumed that at this hour in the morning, Tracy was asleep. But Tracy was far from sleep. Her eyes widened in the dark from the effect of being stunned by the sounds of Monica's moaning.

This was the first time Tracy had ever heard a woman moan out of sexual pleasure. That wasn't on a porno flick. Tracy didn't know whether to remain silent or make a sound to bust Monica's groove. She chose to remain silent. It wasn't that Tracy was enjoying the moment—although, she felt a little queer for listening to another woman masturbate—she just felt that it was Monica's choice to do as she wished with her body.

Twenty minutes later, and ten minutes after Monica was asleep, Tracy slid her hand in her own panties. But unlike Monica, Tracy's moans were carefully muffled.

• • •

FRIENDS

The next morning, Dawn and A'Man ate breakfast in a diner near Dawn's apartment. Although the diner was small, the food was terrific and the place was frequented by many people from throughout the city. On any given Sunday, which was the day it happened to be, you could run into your next-door neighbor or a childhood sweetheart. On this particular day, Dawn ran into Rob, of all people. This was the first time the two of them had seen each other since the breakup between Rob and Tracy.

Moments after A'Man had stepped away from the table, Rob entered the diner. Dawn got his attention and waved him over.

"Hi, Dawn."

"Hello, Robert. Are you still a sucker?"

"Why do you have to disrespect me?"

"You are a sucker for what you did to my girl."

"It's too early in the morning for this."

"That was some dirty shit, fucking Tracy's cousin in her bed."

"Is this why you called me over?"

"No. But you knew that when we saw each other you were going to hear it from me. I hooked you two up."

"Okay. You got that off you chest..."

Although Rob saw A'Man's plate at the table, he still sat across from Dawn. She gave him a look but didn't verbally object.

"How's Tracy doing?"

"She's doing her."

"You look good, Dawn."

Dawn didn't try to hide her smile. It didn't take much to flatter her. In fact, since she had been dating A'Man, her self-esteem had risen.

"You look well yourself."

Before Rob could respond, A'Man walked back over to the table and stood silently, not attempting to mask his anger for Rob, who was sitting in his seat.

"I'm sorry, I'm sitting in your seat."

"Baby, this is Rob. Rob, this is my man A'Man."

"A'Man?" Rob asked.

A'Man gave Rob a nod of acknowledgement.

"Rob used to date my friend...Tracy."

"Tracy?" A'Man asked.

"Yeah. Tracy, the one who's locked up." Dawn said.

"Oh, oh, okay."

"Tracy's locked up?" Rob asked.

"Yeah, but don't let that get out," said Dawn, realizing that she fucked up.

"Yeah? Why is she locked up."

"Something petty. But she won't be in jail long."

After Rob left, Dawn felt bad for letting Tracy's incarceration slip out. But Dawn quickly put it behind her. Unfortunately, the news, like most gossip, spread as fast as it had been uttered. Once Steve got wind of Tracy's incarceration, he would contact an attorney and have him file for immediate custody of Tammy. It would take only a process of elimination for Steve to find out who Tammy was staying with.

CHAPTER
15

A week after her slip of the tongue with Rob, Dawn was in her office, standing close to A'Man. He had one hand on her shoulder while his other hand was rubbing her chin.

"Baby, did you write that check for me?" A'Man asked, gazing down at her.

Dawn paused before speaking. She searched his sparkling brown eyes for a hint of ingratitude; however, she wasn't skillful enough to read his lying eyes.

"Is something on your mind?" asked A'Man.

"No."

"Well, I'm running late, what's up with the check?"

Being a slave to his charm, Dawn could do nothing but reach into her pocketbook and take out her checkbook.

While she leaned over her desk writing out the check, A'Man moved behind Dawn and started rubbing her butt for good measure.

"Can you not do that?"

"I can't touch you?"

"I didn't say that. You're distracting my writing."

"Forget the damn money."

A'Man was acting, he wanted the money. But this was the perfect opportunity for him to test Dawn to see if she would beg him to take her money. A'Man took the check and tore it in half.

"A'Man, I'm sorry," Dawn said.

Suddenly, Sam burst into the office, startling both Dawn and A'Man. For a second, A'Man thought Sam was there to confront him, until she spoke.

"Steve found out Tracy is in jail. Now he's going to file for custody of Tammy!"

"How do you know that?" Dawn asked.

"He just left my house."

"Did he take Tammy?"

"I told him that she wasn't there."

"Shit! Tracy is going to die when she hears this...I have to call a friend who specializes in family court."

Dawn picked up her cell phone and turned her back to Sam and A'Man. While Dawn spoke on the phone, A'Man whispered to Sam, "How are you doing?" She greeted him back with her middle finger. Dawn hung up the phone and turned back around.

"Tracy won't stand a chance in court."

"Shit, I could've told you that!" Sam said.

"Baby, I have to get out of here before that shop closes. Can I have the check?"

As Dawn quickly wrote out another check to get A'Man out of the office, Sam shook her head and scoffed. She had her answer as to why A'Man was with Dawn, it was her money. Sam figured if Dawn couldn't see what was so apparent, then she was a fool who deserved to get played.

"Thank you, baby."

Once A'Man received the check, he gave Dawn a long French kiss while looking over her shoulder at Sam, who turned away in disgust.

After A'Man left, Dawn said boastfully, "He can't keep his hands off of me."

"Do you really like this guy? What do you know about him?"

"I know enough."

"Are you giving him money?"

"My doings with A'Man is my business, okay."

"You're right."

"I'm going to the prison tonight to give Tracy the bad news."

"This is going to break her."

"Well, if you make the bed, you have to lay in it."

"What are you trying to say?"

"The decisions we make in life affect what happens to us. You know what, I have nothing else to say. I have work to do."

Dawn sat at her desk, which was a signal for Sam to leave. Sam walked towards the door to leave, but not before saying in a whisper, "Yeah, make that money for your man."

Dawn looked up, only catching portions of the smart remark.

"What did you say?"

"Nothing."

Jealous bitch, Dawn thought after Sam left.

...

Tracy walked into her cell, drenched in sweat from her four-mile run in the prison yard. The run not only opened Tracy's pores, it also opened her cluttered mind. Running was Tracy's newfound joy. It gave her a feeling of accomplishment; it was a momentary freedom from the stress and boredom of prison life.

"Girl, you are soak and wet," Monica said, tossing Tracy a towel.

"Thanks. Now all I need is a hot shower and a drink."

"Well, the showers are hot. As far as a drink, I have a couple of tea bags."

"Tracy, you got mail," said the guard outside of the cell.

Tracy took the mail with a smile. Her smile faded when she noticed that the return address was from Family Court. Tracy sat at the desk and silently read the petition from Steve's attorney suing for custody of Tammy.

"No!"

"What happened?"

"He wants to take my daughter!"

Tracy handed the petition to Monica, who quickly read the papers and handed them back to Tracy.

"What am I going to do?"

Monica didn't have an answer. All she could do is feel for Tracy.

"He never wanted her! He denied her! Now he's taking advantage of the fact that I'm in jail."

"Tracy, you have a visit," the guard outside the cell said.

"That has to be Sam and Dawn. They probably heard about this shit."

Monica left the cell while Tracy washed quickly at the sink. Afterwards, she hurried to the visiting room. When she got there, she saw Dawn waiting at the reception desk. Actually, Dawn used her lawyer credentials so they could have an official visit in a private area.

"Dawn, what the hell is going on?" Tracy said, sitting across from Dawn.

"How did you hear? Dawn said.

"I received a petition from the court stating that Steve was seeking custody of Tammy."

"I was hoping he didn't file anything and we could work something out among ourselves."

"What's there to work out? He was an absentee father all these years. Tammy is my daughter!"

"And his."

"You're on his side?"

"I'm just stating a fact. His name is on the birth certificate, right?"

"No court in America is going to give Steve custody of my child. Tammy barely knows him."

"Tracy, I am no longer going to speak to you as a friend, I'm now talking as an attorney --"

"Go ahead."

"Let's look at the facts. You are in jail, Steve is on the street, he has a good job, he owns his home, and he is the girl's father."

"Tammy."

"Okay, he's Tammy's father. I'm going to be frank, you're going to lose custody."

Tracy's faint look suggested that if she wasn't sitting down, she would've fallen to the floor.

"Are you saying I'm going to lose my daughter?"

"Tammy will always be your child, but while you remain in here..."

Without bothering to let Dawn complete her sentence, Tracy stood up and walked out from the visit. By the time Tracy reached her cellblock, she was void of emotions. She headed to her cell with a blank look. It was like she was being guided by autopilot.

A few feet away from her cell, Tracy accidentally bumped into a woman who was talking to another prisoner. The woman glared at Tracy, who didn't react.

"You're excused," said the woman.

Tracy didn't respond as she proceeded on her way. The woman felt disrespected in front of her associate.

"Bitch, you heard me talking to you."

By now, Tracy had reached her cell when the woman hurried up to her with the associate trailing behind at a neutral distance.

"You bumped into me."

"Not right now," Tracy responded.

"Who the fuck do you think you are putting on your fucking schedule?"

"My cell is right here if you have a problem. You can step inside and do what you got to do."

Tracy walked in her cell, followed by the woman. Because Tracy was quiet and kept to herself, the woman thought that Tracy was soft, so she felt confident that she could take her. Monica was sitting at the desk. She stood when she saw the two women.

"What's going on?" Monica asked.

"Nothing. I just have to speak with your cellie. Can you step outside for a moment?"

Although Tracy was smiling, Monica could sense that there was some beef between the two women. Nevertheless, she exited the cell and saw the woman's associate waiting by the door. Monica glared at the associate, who turned away to indicate that she didn't want any trouble.

Inside the cell, the woman threw a punch at Tracy but missed. All the rage and anger that resided in Tracy's heart rushed to her fist. From Tracy's first punch, the woman realized that she was in over her head.

Tracy screamed at the woman while she beat her down to the floor. And thanks to the miles Tracy was putting in running, she was in shape. Her stamina prevented any fatigue.

Tracy finally backed off and stared down at the bloody, semiconscious woman on the ground. At first, Tracy felt good, having released her tension out on her foe. But suddenly, she became fearful that she might catch another case. She waited for a moment, then walked out the cell and stepped to the associate.

"Go help that bitch. And she better not tell."

That night, Tracy waited for the guards to take her to the "hole" for the fight. But they never came, because the woman took her ass-whooping like a trooper and kept her mouth shut.

While Monica lay on her bunk, Tracy paced the cell in the dark.

"I don't have a leg to stand on in this custody fight."

"If you lose, this is what's going to happen: when you are released from here, you're going to get your job back with your friend and take those night classes you always talk about. Then you'll fight to get your daughter back. You can't win the fight until you get your shit together. Pacing in the dark and stressing over that which you can't control is not going to help, so stop it."

Monica wasn't finished with her speech, but she stopped talking, expecting a retort from Tracy. But Tracy did the opposite of what was expected of her. Without saying a word, she climbed on her bunk and lay quietly. Monica felt it was nothing left to say, as well, so she turned on her side and fell asleep.

Tracy lay there collecting her thoughts and trying to look at the brighter side of things. But for her, there was no sunny side to losing Tammy.

. . .

With A'Man lying in bed next to her, Dawn sat up with a yellow legal tablet on her lap. Dawn was outlining any negatives or shortcoming in Tracy's life that Steve could bring out against Tracy in the custody case.

Dawn wrote down the little indiscretions and compared them to the big ones. For instance, Tracy and Tammy being homeless and Tracy's stripping came to mind. But Dawn couldn't remember if Tracy danced before or after Tammy was born. Dawn made a note to check on that one.

As the indiscretions began to pile up on the paper, Dawn shook her head at the tough road Tracy had travelled in life.

While Dawn was concentrating on her work before her, A'Man turned on his side, facing her. He reached over and rubbed her leg. She smiled, but removed his hand. He promptly placed it back on her leg.

"Stop, I'm trying to work."

"What are you doing?"

"Something for Tracy concerning legal business. It's confidential."

A'Man turned over and laid on his back, looking like he had an attitude. Dawn glanced at him and thought, *I'm getting tired of this.*

A half-hour later, Dawn laid the legal tablet on it's face and went to the bathroom. A'Man picked up the tablet and read all the details about Tracy's life. He raised an eyebrow when he read that she was a stripper.

CHAPTER
16

In the quiet visiting room, Sam and Dawn sat on either side of Tracy as she bounced Tammy on her lap. Sam's eyes were welled with tears. Tracy choked back her tears, while Dawn sat stone-faced, apparently unaffected by the somber mood.

Tracy had just lost the custody battle over Tammy a couple of hours ago. Although the outcome of the custody suit was a forgone conclusion since Steve filed the petition, when it actually happened, it left Tracy devastated, but she tried to hide it from Tammy.

Although Steve had been victorious, he wasn't popping champagne and celebrating. He had told Tracy that he was only doing what he believed to be in the best interest of his daughter. He wasn't going to treat Tracy as she had treated him early on when he requested to visit Tammy and couldn't.

As a sign of goodwill, and at the request of Dawn and Sam, Steve allowed Tammy to visit Tracy before she moved in with him.

"Tammy, you know you're going to have to live with your father Steve for awhile, until I come home and get a house for us."

"I wasn't bad at Aunt Sam's house," Tammy said, believing that she had done something wrong to be relocated.

"We know that honey," said Sam with a reassuring smile.

"Why do I have to leave?"

"Because Steve is you father and wants you to live with him," Tracy said.

"I told Mommy, I like my father."

"I know baby, and he loves you, too. You're going to be okay." Tracy said.

Tracy stared at Tammy as if she was looking at her for the last time. Tracy's emotions began to swell. To prevent herself from breaking down in front of her child, Tracy changed the topic of the conversation.

"Dawn, how are you and your new man doing?"

"His name is A'Man and he's terrific, but I might be getting tired of him. At the same time, I can't get enough of him."

Sam sucked her teeth with a look of disgust, which drew a reaction from both Tracy and Dawn.

"What was that about?" Dawn asked with attitude.

"Nothing." Sam said.

"It had to be about something, or you wouldn't have sucked your teeth. Say what's on your mind."

"They're my teeth."

"Yes they are. But you sucked them in regards to my business. Say what's on your mind."

With a straight face, Sam lied when she said, "I just don't think this is an appropriate time to talk about men, after what happened today."

"It's okay, I brought it up," said Tracy.

After the visit was over and the hugs and kisses were exchanged, Tracy was expecting the usual goodbye fallout from Tammy, but today was different. After Tammy kissed her mother, she walked to the door with Sam and Dawn, only turning around once to wave the last goodbye.

When Tracy entered her cell after leaving the visit, she collapsed to the floor, while a slow flow of tears slid down her cheeks. Monica kneeled next to Tracy and cuddled Tracy in her arms, rocking her ever so slowly.

"He took my child. My baby girl. I have nothing. I have nothing."

"You have your whole life ahead of you. You're going to get Tammy back, the fight isn't over. You have two months left. We're going to get together when I get out and make things happen. I'll help you with whatever. I care about you, Tracy. Tracy, you matter. You matter."

With each uttering of "you matter," Tracy's slow sobs turned into an uncontrollable tidal wave of tears. This is what she needed, that good cry.

As Monica continued her words of encouragement, she rubbed Tracy's head from front to back, soothing her charred emotions. Although Monica's hands were small and slender, they were filled with love and compassion. From Monica's gentle touch, Tracy closed her eyes, surrendering herself to the moment. This was the most vulnerable and open Tracy had ever been in her life. She began to feel truly loved and relevant. She also felt safe and warm in the arms of a woman who had no agenda or motive but to be a caring friend in a time of need.

CHAPTER

17

The first four months of Tracy's incarceration passed quickly, however, the last two months—following losing custody of Tammy—had been slow, long, and depressing days. But today, at 8:00 a.m., it was all over.

Tracy gave Monica a farewell hug and left the prison as fast as the prison guard could open the door. Outside in the parking lot, Sam was waiting in her car.

"I'm never going back there."

"You wouldn't have been there in the first place if it wasn't for Dawn. Did you ever stop to think that most of your problems were behind her?"

"I've been out of jail five minutes, not now, please."

"You're right. It's time to start off on the right foot. Look in the glove department, it's an envelope in there for you."

Tracy removed the envelope and opened it. She smiled when she saw the money. Tracy didn't bother to count the bills. She was just grateful that she had something to put in her pocket.

Out of the blue, Sam started laughing. Tracy looked at her strangely.

"What's up with you?"

"You get out of jail, and I give you money in an envelope. This is like some Tony Soprano shit."

"Right about now, I wish I was in the mob. I'd probably have about ten of these," said Tracy, patting the envelope.

Twenty minutes later, Sam parked the car in front of Steve's house.

"I don't think I can do this," said Tracy.

"You don't want to see Tammy?"

"Of course I want to see her. I don't think that I can leave here without her."

"I understand, Tracy. I know it just doesn't seem fair, but you can't do anything that would jeopardize you going back to jail. You have six months to walk off."

"I know. I'm just thinking out loud."

Without further delay, Tracy exited the car, smiling as she walked toward Steve's house.

"Tracy," Sam called out.

Tracy jogged back to the car.

"What?"

Sam reached to the back seat and picked up a small bag and handed it to Tracy.

"I picked up a present for Tammy for you. It's a pretty dress and some shoes."

"Thanks," said Tracy with a ton of gratitude on her face.

Tracy knocked softly on Steve's door. When no one answered, she knocked just a bit harder and rang the bell. A minute later, Tracy was pounding on the door and ringing the bell nonstop.

When she came to grips that no on was home, Tracy marched back to the car.

"He knew I was coming today! Is he playing fucking games?"

Tracy got back in the car and looked angrily at Sam.

"Give me your phone."

Tracy called Steve and got his voicemail. She hung up and dialed back.

"Who are you calling now?"

"I'm going to curse Steve out on his voicemail."

"Don't do it. It will hurt you later."

Tracy hung up the phone.

"We're going to wait, okay, Sam?"

A half-hour later, Steve was still a no-show. Tracy said, "Take me to Dawn's office."

When Sam and Tracy entered Dawn's law office, the first thing Tracy noticed was the perky-looking female receptionist.

"Hey, Sam. Dawn's in her office with a client," the receptionist said.

"Thanks."

As Sam and Tracy sat and waited, Tracy occasionally glanced at the receptionist. Tracy felt bad for the girl who was going to have to give up her job.

Ten minutes later, Dawn exited her office with a client. Although Dawn knew that today was Tracy's release date, she wasn't expecting to see her this early. Dawn rushed over to Tracy and hugged her tightly.

"What are you doing here, I thought you would be with Tammy. Where is she?"

"That motherfucker wasn't home. He knew I was coming over."

"Come inside my office."

When the three women entered Dawn's office, Tracy looked around impressed at the transformation of the once bland interior to a more poshly furnished office.

"Did you call Steve?" Dawn asked.

"Yes!"

"Something had to come up. I didn't get the impression that Steve was lying when he said that he wasn't going to prevent you from seeing Tammy, especially on your first day home," said Sam.

"Yeah, I agree," Dawn chimed in.

"Well, where the fuck is he?"

"Do you have any of his friends or relatives' numbers?" Sam asked.

"No. What if something happened with Tammy?" Tracy said worriedly.

"Call your mother. If something was wrong with Tammy, she would know," Sam insisted.

Tracy picked up Dawn's office phone. As she dialed her mother's number, Tracy talked to Sam and Dawn, "I know she told him I was locked up, but I'm wondering how she found out?"

Dawn reacted, but Sam nor Tracy picked it up.

"Hello...yeah, I'm out. Did you talk to Steve today...did he say where he was going? Damn! Oh, did you tell him that I was locked up...well, who told you? Oh, you just heard? I guess a little bird told you huh? Bye!"

Tracy slammed the phone on the receiver. "She talked to Steve, but she doesn't know where he's at. Nor does she know who told her that I was locked up. She don't know shit! I really want to know who told her I was locked up."

"Don't worry about it, move on," Dawn suggested.

"I'll take you back over Steve's later."

"Thanks...Dawn, did you tell the chick out there that I'm getting my job back?"

"I wanted to talk to you about that...Sam, can you give us a moment?"

"Sam doesn't have to go anywhere. What's going on?"

"Well, this is a difficult situation--"

"Here comes the bullshit! You said I could get my job back."

"I know, but right now--"

"Do I still have a room at your apartment?"

"Of course! About the job--"

"I don't want to hear it. Unless you're going to tell me I have a job...just give me a key to your apartment, Dawn."

As Dawn reached in her desk, Sam shot Tracy a look. The two of them shook their heads, sharing the same negative thoughts about Dawn.

"Sam, let's go," Tracy said, taking the key from Dawn.

FRIENDS

"You're wrong, Dawn," said Sam.

Before Dawn could respond, Tracy and Sam were out the door. While Sam and Tracy walked by the receptionist, the receptionist said, "Have a nice day." Neither one of them responded.

Dawn sat at her desk thinking. *The six months Tracy served in jail has changed her.*

Dawn picked up the phone and punched in a number. After six rings, she was about to hang up when A'Man answered.

"Talk. "

"Where are you A'Man? I need for you to pick me up at six...okay, bye...me, too."

...

It was midday. Tracy waited on Steve's porch for him to return home. When Steve and Tammy finally arrived, Steve had a good excuse for not being home earlier; while Tracy was pounding on his door, Steve had taken Tammy to the prison to surprise Tracy, only to learn that she had been released.

Tracy and Tammy's reunion was a heartfelt moment of hugs, tears of joy, and broken laughter, interrupted by declarations of "I love you" uttered by Tracy.

Tracy kneeled in front of Tammy, giving the child a look over. Tammy passed her mother's inspection.

"You even look taller."

Tammy grinned as she raised up on her toes and said, "Now I'm really tall."

"Yes, you are, baby," said Tracy.

Tracy stood and turned toward Steve, who was standing off to the side watching the interaction.

"I want to see her room," Tracy said.

Tracy stepped into Tammy's room, followed by Steve and Tammy. The room was average for a four-year-old girl. Tammy ran and hopped on her bed, while Tracy stood in the center of the room looking around like a social worker.

A female voice came from the hallway, "Steve."

Carol was Steve's new girlfriend. She was standing in the doorway, much to the surprise of Tracy. Tracy looked the girlfriend up and down, not even attempting to mask her disfavor for the intrusion of the woman whose relationship to Steve was obvious when he walked over and gave her a peck on the lips.

"Hey, baby. Carol, this is Tracy, Tammy's mother."

"Nice to finally meet you," Carol said.

"Hi."

"Hey, Tammy," Carol said.

Tammy waved hello and went back to playing with her doll.

"Steve, can I speak with you," Tracy whispered.

Steve followed Tracy into the hallway, while the girlfriend sat on the bed and played with Tammy.

Steve folded his arms across his chest, leaned against the wall, and waited for the onslaught of complaints from Tracy.

"Do she live here?"

"What does that have to do with anything?"

"Don't answer me with a question. Do she live here?"

"No, but what does it matter?"

"You ain't shit!"

"What?"

"You talked all that shit about you wanting me and Tammy to move in with you, but you have a girlfriend."

"I... uh."

"I don't want to hear it. I'm going to spend some time with my daughter and then I'm going home. Tell your girlfriend to give me and my child some privacy, thank you...I don't want my daughter seeing any inappropriate stuff going on over here."

"You had dudes all in your house."

"Dudes?"

"Go see your daughter. Wait a minute."

Steve walked to the door of the bedroom and called his girlfriend out. Together, they walked downstairs. Tracy spent another hour with Tammy, then left without saying goodbye to Steve and his girlfriend.

Tracy walked around the corner to a check cashing store and got a fifty-dollar money order. Her next stop was to a fast-food restaurant before she went to Dawn's apartment. Once she was at the apartment, she went straight to her bedroom. She ate her meal, then wrote a letter to Monica. When she was done, she enclosed the letter and the money order in an envelope to send off the following day.

Ten minutes later, Tracy was basking in a hot bubble bath. The bath was soothing, something she missed while incarcerated.

After the bath, she crawled in bed and fell asleep at 8:00 p.m. Fifteen minutes into her sleep, Tracy was awakened by a soft knock on the door.

"Tracy," said Dawn through the door.

"Come in."

Tracy sat up, while Dawn sat on the bed looking a bit upset.

"What's wrong?" Tracy said.

"Nothing really. I'm still tooting because I told A'Man to pick me up a couple hours ago and he was late. Tracy, I'm glad you're out of that filthy place...about the job..."

"Forget it."

"No, I wanted to tell you at the office that the girl is only going to work for three months, then she's gone. In the mean time, I have a client that owns an upscale restaurant. I got you a job there as a waitress. I know..."

"It's cool. I'm happy to get something so fast."

"Well, you start tomorrow evening...we're going to get Tammy back."

After they talked for another hour, Dawn left Tracy's room. Tracy lay back and smiled, thinking that everything was still on track. Suddenly, Tracy felt horny. As she slid her hand in her panties, she giggled as she thought about that night when she heard Monica moaning from the bottom bunk.

CHAPTER

18

Tracy went to work at the restaurant, which was, in fact, as Dawn had described it, top-notch. It was Tracy's first night and everything was going well until she finished her break and saw Dawn and A'Man seated in her section. Tracy's initial reaction was surprise. Tracy formed a false smile and walked over to Dawn's table.

"Hey, Dawn."

"Good evening, Tracy. This is A'Man. A'Man, this is my friend Tracy."

As Tracy and A'Man exchanged greetings, A'Man noted that Tracy was more beautiful than Dawn had described. He figured Dawn had downplayed Tracy's good looks out of jealousy. Tracy respectfully checked A'Man out. *What is this handsome man doing with Dawn?*

"Do you like the job?" Dawn asked.

"It's a job. What are you ordering?" said Tracy, wishing to get away from the table.

Like she was performing on a stage-play, Dawn changed her voice to super-bourgeois when she said, "A'Man, baby, I'm going to order for you and I, okay? Tracy, I'm going to have...let me see..."

Tracy was incensed. The anger inside her caused her eyes to squint. Clearly, Dawn was showing off, and everyone within earshot could hear. Tracy glanced at A'Man, who looked embarrassed.

CHARLIE BASSETT JR.

While Dawn gave her order, Tracy was seconds away from putting Dawn in her place. But Tracy kept her cool. She kept thinking about what was ultimately at stake: her goal was maintaining employment so she could seek to regain custody of Tammy.

After Dawn and A'Man finished their dinner, Dawn asked Tracy if she needed a ride to the apartment. Although she wasn't feeling Dawn at the moment, Tracy accepted the ride.

When Tracy hopped in the back seat, she borrowed Dawn's cell phone and placed a number of bogus calls to avoid engaging in a conversation with Dawn and A'Man.

Ten minutes into the ride, Tracy overheard Dawn and A'Man in what appeared to be a disagreement over something. A few minutes later, Dawn turned the car onto A'Man's block, double-parking in front of his house.

"You're wrong, Dawn. You own her an apology," A'Man said.

By now, Tracy's full attention was on the conversation.

"Apology for what? It doesn't matter, just get out the car," said Dawn.

"Is this how you talk to me now?"

"No, A'Man. All I'm saying is that I brought you home and it's getting late and I have to work tomorrow."

"You was fronting at the restaurant. If she is really a friend, you would apologize."

Dawn was taken aback for being put on the spot in front of Tracy. But before she could respond, A'Man exited the car and walked towards his house. Tracy was surprised by A'Man's comment. She exited the back seat and got into the passenger seat, but not before glancing at A'Man.

It was like A'Man had eyes in the back of his head, because the moment Tracy had looked at him, he turned back and met her look with a simple nod. A'Man knew from Tracy's look that she had appreciated him sticking up for her. It was exactly what he had planned.

During their ride home, neither Dawn nor Tracy spoke about A'Man's comment. But once they were in the apartment, Tracy turned towards Dawn and said, "Your friend was right, you was fronting at the restaurant."

"Because I speak properly?"

"It was more than just speaking proper. It's how you said things."

"I don't know what to say. I talk like I talk."

With that, Dawn went into her bedroom and called A'Man and gave him a piece of her mind.

Tracy stepped inside her room and called Sam to tell her what had just occurred. But Sam didn't answer her phone, so Tracy decided to write Monica a letter telling her about it.

The next day, while Sam drove Tracy to visit Tammy, Tracy told Sam about the incident at the restaurant and how A'Man had backed her. Sam seemed unimpressed, and once or twice, she slid in a bad word about A'Man. When Tracy asked Sam what did she have against A'Man, Sam responded, "I don't know him, but I don't like him."

CHAPTER
19

Over the weeks since her release from prison, things for Tracy had been pretty consistent. She was visiting Tammy four times a week, working getting overtime hours at the restaurant, and saving every dime when she could. As for her rooming with Dawn, there were the occasional clashes that come with the territory of living with another woman, but there was nothing to cause severe animosity between the two. The only downside of Tracy's life was not spending time with Sam because of their conflicting schedules.

On a stormy Saturday morning, Tracy peered out of her window at the downpouring rain. She sighed heavily at the idea of having to catch public transportation in blustery weather to visit Tammy. Tracy wished she could call Sam for a ride, but Sam was vacationing with her family at Disney World. The only other alternative was to ask Dawn, which Tracy didn't really want to do.

She exited her bedroom and knocked on Dawn's bedroom door. When A'Man opened the door, Tracy was surprised to see him because she didn't know he had spent the night.

"Hey, A'Man."

"What's up, Tracy?"

"Excuse me, Dawn, could you give me a ride over to Steve's house?"

FRIENDS

Dawn walked out of her bedroom into the living room, followed by Tracy with A'Man entering moments later.

"I'm late for an appointment, plus, I'm going in the opposite direction."

"A'Man, do me a favor. Could you drop Tracy off?"

A'Man didn't immediately respond. He looked a bit perturbed, like the ride would be an inconvenience. But he was the least bit daunted. In fact, he had waited weeks for this moment. A legitimate opportunity to be alone with Tracy. A'Man appeared to be contemplating his decision regarding the ride. He was careful not to show his eagerness.

"Where do Steve live?" A'Man asked.

"It's across town. Give her a ride," Dawn asked.

During the ride to Steve's house, Tracy struck up a friendly conversation about the weather to pass the time and lighten the stale atmosphere in the car. A'Man, however said very little, only responding with a brief reply or a nod of his head. This is how the ride went until A'Man pulled in front of Steve's house.

"This is it, right?" A'Man asked.

"Yes. I really appreciate the ride, I didn't want to catch the bus in this weather."

"I feel you. I didn't have anything on the agenda today anyway."

"Take it easy, A'Man, thanks again."

He loved how she said his name. Tracy opened the car door to exit but paused for a moment, then closed the door back.

"Oh, I also want to thank you for what you said to Dawn that night when we left the restaurant."

"That wasn't about nothing. I'm straight up. If I see something wrong, I speak on it...how long are going to be?"

"Excuse me?"

"Do you need me to wait?"

"I might be a couple of hours. I'll try to catch a ride if it's still raining. If it's not, I'll probably end up taking the bus."

"I'm going to give you my cell number. If you need a ride, you can call me."

"That's okay."

"No, take the number. Like I said, I'm not doing nothing today. I'm just going home to chill. I have to go back to the apartment anyway."

"Okay," Tracy said hesitantly.

After she put A'Man's number in her phone, she called Steve and told him to open the door. A'Man and Tracy sat in silence while waiting for Steve to come to the door. Seconds later, the front door opened. Tracy said goodbye to A'Man and dashed towards the house.

A'Man drove to the popular diner where he and Dawn had eaten at before. While he sat at the table waiting for his order, he thought about Tracy: how sexy she looked when she wore her sweatpants around the apartment, and how sweet she smelled when he passed her. He thought about the day he watched her brush her hair in the bathroom when the door was ajar and how beautiful she had looked. He couldn't wait to sleep with her. He felt confident that it would happen.

As for his relationship with Dawn, it was going downhill. And since she had cut back on the money and gifts she was giving him, there was no other need to stick around but to be close to Tracy.

The fact that A'Man was attempting to play with fire didn't much matter. He had to have Tracy at any cost. Ever since he had read the things Dawn wrote about Tracy on the legal tablet, A'Man's curiosity about her piqued his interest in her sexually. Once she was released from prison and he saw her in the flesh, it was lights out.

To learn more about Tracy without appearing to be interested in her, A'Man picked Dawn very cleverly for information, attaining a little bit at a time. He was so good at his task; he would say one word about an issue, and Dawn would run her mouth about herself or Sam and Tracy. The most valuable information he discovered was that Tracy wasn't seeing anyone, and she didn't have sex in over six months. That little discovery had A'Man's juices going. He desperately wanted to be the recipient of Tracy's built-up sexual tension when she finally released it.

A'Man nodded his head confidently. If he played his cards right, he would have Tracy soon. He chuckled. *How many guys banged three best friends in less than a year?*

A'Man was so engulfed in his egotistical obsession that he didn't notice that Rob and Joann had entered the restaurant and were walking by him. Rob stopped when he recognized A'Man.

"Yo, what's up?" Rob said.

A'Man looked up, surprised to see Rob and the pretty, young woman at his side.

"Hey, what's happening?"

A'Man stood from the table and shook Rob's hand. Joann, standing slightly behind Rob, checked A'Man out. From the look in her eyes, he could tell that she liked what she saw. In return, A'Man checked Joann out in a glance. *Cute, young, but legal.*

When the waitress brought over A'Man's food, the men exchanged quick pleasantries and said their goodbyes. Rob and Joann took a table at the far end of the diner with Rob seated with his back to A'Man, while Joann sat in his direction.

Cleverly and unbeknownst to Rob, A'Man and Joann made a connection with their eyes. When Joann went to the bathroom, she wrote her phone number on a napkin. On the way back to her table she dropped the balled up napkin at the feet of A'Man.

A'Man picked up the napkin. But before he uncreased it, his cell phone rang. He looked at the strange number on his phone and was about to ignore the call, then he thought it might be Tracy. He answered the phone and smiled when he heard her voice. She asked A'Man if he could he give her a ride home if it wasn't any trouble.

While Joann was telling Rob how much she loved him, A'Man walked over to their table with a folded napkin in hand. He presented the napkin to Rob.

"I want to give you this number."

Joann looked stunned with her mouth agape. She thought A'Man was a player, and she couldn't believe that he was about to give her up. Rob took the napkin and read the number with no expression that Joann could detect. She wondered why he wasn't snapping or cursing her out.

"Alright, I'll put it in my phone."

"My number is--," Rob said.

A'Man held up his hand, cutting him off, "Yo, I have to go. Just give me a call and give it to me then. Maybe we can do something with the girls."

Rob looked away from A'Man as he put the napkin in his pocket. That provided A'Man the opportunity to wink his eye at Joann. She blushed. *This guy is smooth.*

"Alright, I'll see you later," Rob said.

Joann couldn't wait for A'Man to call her so she could curse him out for playing with her.

When A'Man picked Tracy up, he practiced the same quiet routine as he had performed when he drove her to Steve's house. Once again, Tracy struck up a conversation to pass the time. In the middle of their nearly one-sided conversation, A'Man asked, "Do you mind if I make a stop?"

"You're the driver."

A'Man stopped the car and jogged over to an unassuming rowhouse and disappeared inside. While he was in the house, Tracy nodded her head to the music while thinking. *A'Man is a cool dude.*

When they arrived at the apartment, A'Man followed Tracy inside. Dawn wasn't home—which wasn't a surprise—but Tracy suddenly realized that this was the first time she was ever alone in the apartment with A'Man. For a second, she wondered why that fact even came to mind.

Instinctively, she turned to go into her bedroom, while A'Man took off his jacket and intentionally let an ounce of weed in a clear, plastic baggy fall from his jacket pocket. He pretended not to notice it and walked into Dawn's bedroom and closed the door behind him.

Tracy picked up the weed and examined it. From visual inspection, she could see that it was the good stuff that she used to smoke. She had quit while in jail, but now with the product in her hand, she was having second thoughts.

As the weed began to call her, she fought the temptation and knocked on Dawn's bedroom door. A'Man opened the door with his shirt unbuttoned. Tracy couldn't help but get a peek at his six-pack. When A'Man saw Tracy, he told her to hold on one second. He closed the door and buttoned up his shirt. This was all staged. A'Man knew Tracy was going to return the weed, so he had the peep show ready for her.

A few seconds later, A'Man opened the door with his clothes in order. Tracy complimented herself for her earlier assessment that A'Man was a good dude. Little did she know, he was orchestrating the scenario that she was unknowingly walking into.

"You dropped this," Tracy said.

"Damn. Good looking out. If Dawn would've found this, I wouldn't have heard the last of it."

"You got that right. It look like that good shit."

"Definitely."

A'Man walked out of the bedroom and put the weed back in his jacket pocket.

"I used to smoke."

"I know," A'Man uttered. He made it look like it was a slip of the tongue.

Tracy looked seriously at A'Man. He averted his eyes and sat on the sofa, placing his hands over his face. Tracy walked over and stood in front of him.

"What do you mean, you know?"

"Aw, man."

"No, A'Man. You said you were straight up. How do you know I used to smoke weed?"

"I'm not trying to start no shit...if I tell you something, promise me that you won't repeat it."

"It depends on what it is."

"Since you won't promise..."

A'Man stood up and turned towards Dawn's bedroom. Tracy reached out and arrested his arm.

"Wait!"

"I told you, you have to promise me," A'Man said in a voice that expressed his need for Tracy to make an oath to him.

Tracy looked in A'Man's seemingly sincere eyes, and for some reason, she felt the need to trust him. Whether it was his voice, his eyes, or curiosity, Tracy said, "I promise."

I knew you would.

"Do you consider Dawn a friend?"

"Yes," said Tracy cautiously.

A'Man chuckled. Tracy's eyes widened as she asked, "She was talking about me wasn't she?"

"Why did I open my mouth! I'm not trying to turn you against her. But lately, Dawn has been getting on my ass for smoking weed and not working right now. And every time she start with the weed thing, she brings you up. She starts talking about my girlfriend Tracy is the same way."

Tracy looked astounded.

"But she didn't say it in a derogatory way." A'Man said.

A'Man could see from Tracy's expression that she was pissed. Even more so than what he expected. He smiled, knowing he had lit a fire that would soon burn away Tracy and Dawn's friendship, and he would be there with open arms, waiting for Tracy.

A'Man walked into Dawn's room and left Tracy in the living room simmering in anger. A'Man stood in the room a moment, allowing Tracy to get worked up, then he returned to the living room. By now Tracy was sitting on the sofa. He placed a hand on her shoulder and said, "Don't worry about it. It's no big deal. Dawn looks down upon me, too."

Afterward, A'Man left the apartment. He knew he had crossed the line, but he was willing to gamble that Tracy was going to keep her promise and not say a word to Dawn.

Later that evening, when Dawn came home she brought Chinese food for her and Tracy. Dawn noticed Tracy looked upset.

"What's wrong?"

"Nothing."

"Are you sure?"

"Yes."

"Well, I got you some Chinese food."

Although Tracy was upset with Dawn, Tracy took the food under the premise of "fuck you!"

As the weeks followed, Dawn and Tracy's relationship became strained, while Tracy and A'Man began to converse more. A'Man kept things on a platonic level, careful not to let any innuendoes slip out that would indicate how he felt about Tracy. Dawn, who was caught up in her work, didn't notice the change in her and Tracy's relationship or how close Tracy and A'Man had become. As far as Sam being caught in the thick of things, she pretty much kept her distance from the apartment to avoid running into A'Man.

It was a warm Friday evening and A'Man had just received a call from Dawn. She was letting him know that she was going to be working late, so he decided that it was time to test the water and see how close he and Tracy had become. Although neither one of them ever said or hinted at anything inappropriate, he could sense that she liked him.

When A'Man got to the apartment, Tracy was in the kitchen drinking a beer from a six-pack on the table. She had just returned from Steve's house, only to discover that when she went there, Steve had taken Tammy out of town for the weekend. Now Tracy was trying to drown out her depression with the beer.

This is what A'Man and all slimy males lived for, the opportunity to lift the spirits of a damsel in distress. When A'Man walked into the kitchen, the first thing he noticed were Tracy's puffy, red eyes.

"What's wrong, Tracy?" he said, taking a seat across from her.

"That rotten motherfucker took my daughter out of town without telling me."

"People can be so inconsiderate. I know how much you love your daughter. I see how hard you're working, and you visit her all the time. How could he not let you know something like that?"

"All he had to do is pick up the phone and say me and Tammy are going away. It would've been cool."

As Tracy started to cry, A'Man circled the table and rubbed her shoulder. As he consoled her, Tracy thought back to how Monica consoled her, and how she was slowly developing those same feelings she felt on that night.

"Dawn never shows emotions. All she does is bitch to me. I feel so bad for you about your child. I wanted a baby with Dawn, but she doesn't want children. How can I be with a woman who doesn't want children?"

A'Man sat down next to Tracy and continued to vent about Dawn. Tracy saw his eyes welled tears. She patted his back and told him that everything will be okay because he was a good man. A'Man smiled inside. He had successfully turned the table, making himself be the one in need of consoling.

"Do you want one of these?" Tracy said.

She handed A'Man a can of beer, but he shook his head no.

"Dawn and I are done, this is it. I can't put up with this no longer."

A'Man pulled out a plastic bag of an ounce of weed and started rolling.

"What are you doing?" Tracy said surprisingly with a smile.

"Dawn ain't going to be home until late. Fuck it, I need my medicine."

Tracy chuckled as she eyeballed the weed.

"I can't do shit right in her eyes and I know she sleeping around."

"No she isn't."

"She's a fucking fraud. She asked me to give you a ride, then she bitches later. Asking questions, 'Do you like Tracy?' You know she jealous of you because you're beautiful."

Tracy wasn't too drunk to let the statement fill her head up. She knew she looked good, and she was wary when a girlfriend's man complimented her while putting his own woman down. But this evening, she let the compliment slide.

As A'Man began to smoke the weed, he pretended to be more high than he actually was, becoming more talkative. Smelling the weed was too much for Tracy, so she asked for some. While they sat at the table getting high, Tracy suddenly became paranoid and told A'Man she was going in her room to smoke. When he followed her to the door, Tracy shook her head "no" but A'Man talked himself into the room. A'Man sat in a chair, while Tracy laid across the bed.

As the weed began to make A'Man feel good, he began to reveal more secrets about Tracy that he learned from the tablet, claiming that Dawn had told him about them. Once again, he made Tracy promise not to confront Dawn. Once again, she promised. By now, Tracy was slowly beginning to really dislike Dawn.

"Yeah, she jealous of you. She's just mad that nobody would pay to see her dance or ask for a lap dance."

Tracy looked surprised, "She told you I used to dance?"

"What do you say when I tell you something?"

"I'm not going to say nothing...I promise."

"Shit, I don't care. I wished I was in that club to check you out."

"No you didn't, I was bad. I only danced for a week."

"I used to dance," A'Man said.

A'Man stood and started gyrating his hips. Tracy burst into laughter. As he continued, he made his way directly in front of Tracy. For the first time, she began to look at him differently. No longer in her eyes was he her girlfriends man; he was a sexy man dancing seductively for her. The more she smoked and watched A'Man, the hornier she became.

Then without warning, A'Man leaned forward and kissed her lips. He stepped back and waited for her reaction. She sat still, staring into his eyes. He reached out and cupped her face in his hands and kissed her again.

It was like something came over Tracy. She snatched off her clothes and helped him with his. Tracy fucked A'Man with the fire and passion that he had expected. She grunted loudly, kissed him hard, and rode him with the speed of a cheetah. A'Man could barely keep up. It was the best sex he had ever experienced. She felt no shame or remorse.

After they kissed, A'Man left the room and took a shower. Afterwards, he hopped into Dawn's bed. Tracy cleaned and aired out the kitchen.

When Dawn entered the apartment, a feeling washed over her. She couldn't put her finger on it, but she felt something. She climbed in bed with A'Man. They began to kiss. Then Dawn ducked her head underneath the covers and went down on him while A'Man thought about Tracy.

The next morning, while Tracy was headed to the bathroom, A'Man was exiting the bathroom. The pair touched each other's hands like secret lovers passing in the night. An hour later, while A'Man, Dawn, and Tracy were in the living room, Dawn thought she picked up on some extra eye contact between Tracy and A'Man. Dawn, nevertheless, dismissed it with the belief that Tracy would never cross her with A'Man.

It had been a week after Tracy and A'Man's first hookup. And each day since, it had been more of the same. Sex in Tracy's bedroom, A'Man's house, and even once in Dawn's own bed. Tracy considered that payback for Dawn being the cause of her going to jail.

One day, A'Man and Tracy finished making love in his bedroom. As they lay in each other's arms, Tracy gazed into A'Man eyes, while he wooed her with sweet nothings. After being fed dishes of lies, sex, and A'Man sucking on her like a taffy, Tracy was hooked.

"When are you going to let Dawn know?"

"Soon. This is a difficult situation."

"I'm going to tell her myself, because I don't like this sneaking around."

"You can't tell her, it has to come from me, but I have to take care of something with her first."

"You're not going to be sleeping with the both of us...did you hear something?" said Tracy, sitting up.

"No."

"A'Man!" Dawn yelled as she walked up the stairs.

"Shit! That's Dawn," Tracy said.

A'Man looked fearfully surprised. He hopped out of the bed and slipped his pants on while Tracy lay in bed as if she was waiting for this moment.

"Get in the closet!"

"Fuck no!"

As A'Man spoke rapidly, pleading with Tracy to get into the closet, he snatched her clothes from the floor and handed them to her. Tracy took her time getting out of bed.

"I don't want it to go down like this. I told you I have to get something first before I tell her about us."

"I don't care," said Tracy, standing in place and looking defiant.

Just as the door was opening, A'Man gave Tracy a desperate look, but it was too late for Tracy to reach the closet, so she slid underneath the bed seconds before Dawn walked in. A'Man walked over to Dawn, meeting her at the door. He hugged her and kissed her on the cheek. Tracy heard A'Man's lips smack from the kiss and was washed over with jealousy.

"What are you doing here?"

"I didn't have to be in court, so I wanted to surprise you."

Dawn walked over to the bed and sat on the edge a few inches away from Tracy. As Tracy lay among the dust, she felt like a first-class fool in more ways than one. There she was, supposed to be the love of A'Man's life, and she was the one hiding. Her dignity as a woman had taken a blow.

"What is that smell?" Dawn said.

Dawn stood up and placed her hands on her hips as she started looking around the room. Tracy felt offended at the implication that Dawn might be referring to her.

"What smell?" A'Man asked.

"It smells like sex."

A'Man chuckled nervously, "You're tripping."

"No, it smells like somebody was fucking."

"It's probably my sweat. I was just working out hard."

"If you smell like that when you exercise, maybe you need to see a doctor because something is wrong with you."

"If something is wrong with me, something have to be wrong with you as well."

The words hit Tracy in the gut. She thought about not using protection with A'Man and wished she had. All at once, there was no sound in the room. Tracy wondered what was going on. Suddenly, she heard a door swing open. For a second, she thought that A'Man and Dawn had left the room. Tracy was about to crawl from underneath the bed until she heard A'Man laughing.

"Girl, you're really tripping. There's nobody in the closet."

"Well, I have to check."

"Give me a kiss?"

"Don't try to kiss me until you take a shower."

Tracy was hot as she listened. She couldn't wait to ask A'Man how could he want to kiss Dawn while she was underneath the bed.

"Come take a shower with me."

"No. I don't need a shower."

"Come on, we can have some fun."

A'Man only asked Dawn to take a shower with him to get her out the bedroom so Tracy could make her exit. But how could Tracy have known his intent? Listening to her lover beg another woman to bathe with him had Tracy's blood boiling. She felt betrayed, she felt like an idiot. She could no longer play the role of a scared mouse in hiding, so she crawled from beneath the bed. If she would've waited five seconds longer, Dawn would've followed A'Man to the shower and the confrontation would've been avoided.

"What the fuck!"

Dawn yelled when she saw the person crawl from under the bed. When she saw that it was Tracy, Dawn initially chuckled at the ridiculous sight of Tracy with dust on her face. But Dawn's amusement was short-lived, very short-lived.

As the reality of what was occurring, and what had obviously taken place before her arrival, set in, Dawn was crushed. She couldn't speak. While Tracy dressed quickly, A'Man placed his hands on Dawn's shoulders and turned her away from glaring at Tracy to facing him.

"I'm so sorry," A'Man said.

"I felt that y'all was doing something, but I said no, Tracy's my friend, she wouldn't do this to me."

"This was not about you," Tracy said.

"How could it not be about me? You're sleeping with my man. I opened my home to you."

"I'm not trying to hear this. A'Man, tell her to leave."

"No, you leave my apartment," said Dawn.

"I will!"

"I guess you love him, right?" Dawn said.

"A'Man loves me. Not you, me. Look at you."

Dawn turned and looked at A'Man with tears in her eyes.

"I hate you. Tell that broke bitch to give you the five hundred dollars you need for your car."

"He don't need your money."

"Tracy, be quiet. Let me handle this," A'Man said.

"It's nothing to handle. Tracy, you're stupid. He don't have shit but a big dick. You don't have shit either. I guess y'all go good together."

Tracy rushed over to Dawn to attack her, but A'Man restrained her.

"Let me go, I'm going to knock this bitch out," Tracy said.

"Try it...I don't have time for this. I'm out and I'm not even mad. Tracy, I see why you always fuck up, because you're always making bad choices."

Dawn put on a brave face and left the house. Tracy pulled away from A'Man.

"Why didn't you tell her that you love me?"

"It doesn't matter, it's over between Dawn and me."

Dawn sat in her parked car sobbing. Her stomach was in knots. It felt like she was trying to give birth through her navel. No matter how much she told herself that she didn't care, she did care. The more she fought the pain in her stomach, the more intensified the pain became. Finally, she started her car and drove home.

Meanwhile, back at A'Man's bedroom, Tracy stood in front of a timid-looking A'Man with her finger in his face.

"You fucked me then asked Dawn to take a shower with you! What were you going to do, take her in the shower and fuck her after you just got finished sleeping with me?"

"I was trying to get her out the room so you could leave...she's gone, why are we fighting?"

A'Man placed his hands on Tracy's waist and pulled her close to him. She stepped back away from his grasp and placed her hand on her forehead.

"What am I doing?" said Tracy as her conscious began to speak to her.

But A'Man wasn't going to allow Tracy to have second thoughts about their relationship. He rushed over to her. This time he held her tighter and placed her head in his chest.

"We made this decision to be together because we are in love. Aren't you in love with me?"

Tracy nodded her head "yes."

"Well, let me hear you say it."

"I'm in love with you, A'Man."

"I love you, too."

"I have to go get my things from Dawn's house."

"No. If you go over there, there's going to be a fight, and I won't have you going back to jail. I'll go."

"Absolutely not. I'll call Sam."

Hearing Sam's name caused A'Man to flinch. The last thing he needed was for Sam to enter the fray. Tracy looked at A'Man suspiciously.

"Why did you react when I mentioned Sam's name?"

"I don't know. I just don't want everybody in our business. We don't need the extra drama."

"Sam isn't extra drama, she's my best friend."

Tracy grabbed the phone and called Sam. A'Man sat on the edge of the bed and followed the conversation.

"Hi, Sam, I need you to go over to Dawn's house and pick up my stuff, everything is in my room. I moved out. We had a fight...I'm staying with A'Man...yes, A'Man."

Tracy held the phone away from her ear as Sam screamed and yelled.

"I'll tell you later, it's a long story. Can you just go get my shit before that bitch burns my clothes or throws them out."

After Tracy hung up the phone, she milled about, justifying in her mind why she crossed Dawn. A'Man sat silently watching Tracy. For a moment, he thought about telling her about the affair with Sam, but he retracted the thought, remembering Sam's threat and her adamant intentions on keeping the one-night stand a secret.

On the sadder part of town, Dawn entered her apartment feeling like the loneliest woman in the world. Although her relationship with A'Man had been on the rocks, Dawn never imagined that they would break up in the near future. And now that Tracy had him, Dawn wanted A'Man more than ever.

Dawn walked in Tracy's bedroom while taking stock of her belongings, which wasn't much. "She doesn't even have shit!"

Dawn started to trash Tracy's things, but she didn't have the energy nor did she want to put her hands on anything that Tracy had touched except for, of course, A'Man.

Dawn walked into the living room and sat on the sofa, drowning in her sorrow. If she could, she would've traded the success she had accomplished in life to be beautiful so she could rival Tracy for the affections of A'Man.

Dawn tried to pinpoint just how Tracy had won A'Man over her. She first suspected that Tracy told him about the affair with Mr. Hall and the abortion without first telling David that she was pregnant.

"That's what the bitch did! Made me look like a whore!"

Next, Dawn began to beat herself up for not giving A'Man the five hundred dollars he had asked for last week. She even suspected that Tracy was probably letting A'Man have sex with her in the butt, something Dawn consistently denied A'Man each time he asked.

That nasty bitch, Dawn thought.

But sitting there the loser, Dawn wished she had accommodated A'Man's every wish and desire.

Minutes later, Dawn's sadness turned to anger, the kind of anger that inspires a woman to fight for her man by any means necessary.

Dawn marched into the kitchen and grabbed the first weapon she saw, a sparkling butcher's knife in the sink. She didn't have intentions on killing Tracy, but she wanted a weapon in her hand. If push came to shove, she would stab Tracy in the arm or another nonvital part of her body.

As Dawn walked out of the kitchen, she looked at the knife and realized it was too big, so she replaced it with a steak knife.

Dawn grabbed her car keys and hurried out of the apartment, but before she exited the apartment complex, she saw Sam outside ringing the bell. Dawn opened the door, stepped to the side and let Sam enter. From the look on Sam's face, Dawn assumed that Sam was dealing with a crisis of her own, or she had spoken to Tracy.

"Whose side are you on?" Dawn snapped.

Before Sam could fire back, she saw Dawn holding the steak knife at her side. For the first time in their fifteen years of friendship, Sam was frightened of Dawn.

"Dawn, what are you doing with that knife?"

"I'm going to get that bitch! I let her in my house and she makes a fool of me!"

"Dawn, let's go inside your apartment and talk?"

"No, you talk some sense into Tracy's head, she the one that needs a good talking to. And you can do it at the hospital, because I'm going to stab that bitch!"

A neighbor entered the complex. He spoke to Dawn, then he saw the knife in her hand, so he promptly kept stepping. Sam could see Dawn's embarrassment.

"Give me the knife."

Dawn hesitated for a moment, then she reluctantly handed Sam the knife. They both turned around and entered Dawn's apartment. Dawn flopped down on the sofa, Sam sat next to her.

"What happened?"

Dawn sighed heavily, cleared her throat, and said, "Last week I thought I saw something between A'Man and Tracy, but I dismissed it. You know, Tracy supposed to be my girl. I just knew she wouldn't creep with my man. Today, I leave work early to surprise A'Man. Our relationship was slipping. I see why now, it was because of Tracy. Anyway, I goes to his house. When I walked in the bedroom, it smelled like somebody was fucking. I'm not stupid. I open the closet, nobody is in there. This motherfucker said I was smelling his sweat from him working out. While he was trying to get me to take a shower with him, the next thing I know, this nasty bitch come crawling from under the bed like a damn cat."

Sam shook her head at how pitiful Tracy probably looked and had become.

"At first, I laughed because the bitch looked stupid. Then it sunk in that I was the stupid one."

"You're not stupid."

"Sam, you and I fight all the time, and I know you would never do something like that to me. And I would never do that to you or Tracy. Women are suppose to have rules. Don't touch nobody's man, even if you dealt with him in the past. I know some women say it's cool to deal with an ex if you get permission. Fuck that! Keep the borders in place to eliminate any bullshit later on. If I met a man and found out that you dealt with him, I'm breaking up with the guy. You're my girl. You know what I mean?"

Sam was speechless. She felt like more of a betrayer than Tracy was. Sam knew if she had confided in her friends about the one-night stand with A'Man, none of this would've taken place. Sam was now holding herself responsible for the rift between Dawn and Tracy.

"Sam, the bad part of all this is that I still love him. I want him back. Tracy better make the best of her time with him, because I'm going to fight for my man...Sam, am I a fool?"

"No. you're not a fool. You're just a woman in love. But you can't let love make you do a foolish thing because then you become a fool...Tracy called me to get her things."

"I don't care what happens from this point, she can't move back here and don't let that foul bitch move in with you. She can't be trusted."

After delivering some encouraging words and stressing patience, Sam hugged Dawn, then she left and drove to A'Man's house. Although there was a parking spot in front of A'Man's house, Sam parked down the block because she didn't want A'Man to see her if he came to the door with Tracy. After she parked, she waited for a moment to clear her thoughts. Once she was ready, she called Tracy and told her to come to the car.

"Hey, Sam, you got my stuff?"

"Tracy, how could you do this?"

"I don't want to talk about it."

"Our friendship is not worth discussing this?"

Tracy sighed, "It started a couple of weeks ago. I was feeling bad, A'Man consoled me. We started smoking weed, one thing led to another, and here we are."

"How could you sleep with Dawn's man?"

"A'Man is my man."

"You know what I mean. Dawn is your friend."

Tracy gave Sam a look.

"She wasn't my friend when she was talking all that shit about me to him."

"So what? You fell for that? You know damn well if a guy is trying to get in your pants, he's going to say shit like: Dawn doesn't like you, she talks behind your back, she said you're this and that. That's the oldest game in the world besides pointing out another person's inaccuracies so you can look better. Come on, Tracy."

"It's more to our relationship than that. A'Man said that I can stay with him, and he's going to help me get Tammy back and take care of us."

"Take care of you how? That motherfucker is thirty years old and don't have a job."

"Don't call him a motherfucker!"

Sam was caught off guard by Tracy's vigorous defense of A'Man.

"Tracy, you can't sit back and wait for A'Man to take care of you."

"I know, I'm just stating what he's going to do."

"What he said he would do, there's a difference."

"I'm not going to sit here and play semantics with you."

"What about Dawn?"

"What about her? Do I feel bad, yes, a little. But after what A'Man told me, I shouldn't feel shit for Dawn. She must have told him every negative thing I did in life."

"Did he tell you all this before or after he fucked you?"

"Why are you hating on us."

"Please!" Sam scoffed.

"Sam, I love him. He's the best man I ever had. We're getting married...not right away. Probably next year. Tammy is going to look so pretty at our wedding."

As Sam stared at Tracy in disbelief, she recalled the sex with A'Man was good, but not good enough to make a woman go instantly crazy. Sam thought that six month jail term had altered Tracy's thinking and common sense.

"If A'Man is such a wonderful guy, why would he cheat with his girlfriend's best friend?"

"It wasn't like that..."

"The man ain't shit! He's dirty!"

As Sam and Tracy's conversation moved to a heated argument about A'Man worthiness, Sam blurted out, "I slept with A'Man!"

Tracy was seized frozen by Sam's admission. She stared at her friend. She was caught between believing her or smacking Sam for lying. It wasn't Sam intentions to ever reveal the affair, but it slipped out. Since it had, Sam hoped that it would open Tracy's eyes to see A'Man for the man he truly was, a dog.

"You're lying," said Tracy in a scratchy voice.

"Ask him. The one-night stand I told you I had was with A'Man."

"Why would you lie like this?"

"Ask him."

Tracy exited the car, slamming the door. Sam watched Tracy enter A'Man's house, then she pulled off. Although the affair was now in the public domain, Sam still wasn't going to come clean to Andrew. If he did find out about it, she figured she would cross the bridge when she came to it.

When Tracy entered A'Man's house, he was waiting for her in the living room, and from her deer-in-the-headlights glare, he assumed Sam had told her about the affair.

"Where are your clothes? I had a feeling Dawn was going to do something crazy!"

Tracy was silent and unresponsive as she stared at A'Man. He wrestled with telling the truth or lying when Tracy eventually asked whether he slept with Sam or not. Sure enough, Tracy presented that question in a calm voice, "Did you sleep with Sam?"

A'Man looked offended as he took a step towards Tracy and gazed into her sad eyes. He asked himself, should he employ the rules of a politician: deny, deny, deny, when confronted with questions of whether he engaged in an affair. *I didn't have sexual relations with that woman.* A'Man thought about mimicking former President Bill Clinton, but A'Man settled for, "Tracy, how could you ask me something like that?"

"Did you fuck Sam?" Tracy yelled.

"No!" said A'Man as he turned away from her, "That's why I didn't want you to call her. I had a feeling something like this would happen!"

"But she said y'all had sex."

A'Man faced Tracy and placed his hands on her shoulders and said, "From day one, Sam didn't like me. So she will say anything to break us up."

A'Man could see that Tracy wasn't buying it.

"I tell you the truth and you brush it off. You know what? I see whose word carry weight with you."

"Why would she lie?"

Calmly, A'Man said, "I was just with Dawn, now I'm with you." This time he raised his voice, "If you think I'm lying, get the fuck out of my house, because I don't want to be with a woman who doesn't trust or believe in me! But if you believe that Sam is lying, then stay! Because she is!"

A'Man had called Tracy's bluff, and to add credence to his farce, he walked over to the door and opened it, then he folded his arms across his chest, waiting for Tracy to make the next move. Tracy lowered her head, pondering her next move. Moments later, she made up her mind. She closed the door and walked into A'Man's waiting embrace.

CHARLIE BASSETT JR.

"I love you, A'Man. Everyone is going to hate our relationship."

"You have to expect that Sam, Dawn and the other haters are going to say and do anything to keep us apart."

"I know, baby. I'm sorry."

CHAPTER
20

On a cloudy Friday afternoon, a depressed-looking Dawn sat at her office desk, scribbling A'Man's name repeatedly on a notepad. It had been two weeks since she last spoke with him on that unforgivable day that she discovered Tracy and A'Man's relationship.

What Dawn didn't realize at the time was that her yearning to be with A'Man wasn't because of love, it was, rather, that age-old conflict known as female rivalry. On an impulse, she picked up the phone and called A'Man. When he didn't answer, she left the following message on his voicemail:

"Hello, A'Man, this is Dawn. I'm just calling to say we need to talk. I know things haven't been well between us, but I believe we can work things out. A'Man, I love you. I know I denied you many things, but I'm going to change...I was thinking about it...and...you can stick it anywhere you like. I know I told you before that I would never do it...you know what I'm talking about, and the rough sex you like, I'm ready. Please call me back...and the money..."

Suddenly, Dawn realized that she was disgracing herself as a feminist. She quickly hung up the phone and prayed that A'Man would erase the message without listening to it. Even worse, allowing Tracy to listen to it.

As Dawn sat there wishing she could take back her message, she wondered how could she have let herself fall to such a deplorable low for A'Man who was nothing more than a handsome face.

•••

Two miles away at Chuck E. Cheese's, A'Man was spending quality time with Tracy and Tammy. When he was exiting the men's room, his cell phone rang. He looked at Dawn's number and smiled. Although he wasn't in the presence of Tracy, he allowed the call to go to voicemail with the intentions on calling Dawn back later. Seconds after Dawn's call, he received a call from Joann. He let that call go to voicemail as well. Since Joann had slipped him her number, they had been communicating by phone, but they didn't get together in person, as of yet.

Gloating over his two caller's interest in him, A'Man walked back over to the area where Tracy and Tammy were and kissed Tracy on her cheek. Tammy saw the kiss and frowned. As the day carried on, everyone in Chuck E. Cheese's was enjoying themselves, save A'Man. For each time he tried to play with Tammy, she ran and hid behind her mother. Tracy whispered to A'Man that Tammy would come around, he smiled understandingly. But inside he felt like a bogeyman for having a four-year-old child run away from him.

Later that evening, A'Man and Tracy dropped off Tammy, then they went home. While A'Man showered, Tracy cooked dinner. Twenty minutes later, A'Man entered the kitchen dressed for a night on the town.

"Why are you dressed up?" Tracy asked.

"I have to go out and take care of some business."

"Dressed like that? I cooked dinner."

"I'm sorry, baby. I'll get a plate when I get in. I won't be late."

"It's already late."

A'Man moved to Tracy and placed his hands on her waist. Tracy stepped back from him.

"What kind of business you have to take care?"

"You said you trust me, now you're questioning me. This ain't going to work if you continue to question my every move."

Caught off guard by A'Man's suggestion that their relationship wasn't going to work if she asked him questions, Tracy was slow to respond. Before she formulated a response, A'Man was out the door. Tracy turned off the stove and dumped the pot of food in the sink.

A'Man sat in the car, smiling as he listened to Dawn's message to get back together and her offer to allow him to "stick it anywhere." Although the idea of A'Man exploring Dawn's "forbidden zone" was intriguing, he had a more interesting proposal from Joann.

When A'Man arrived at Joann's, she answered the door clad in a miniskirt, no stockings or shoes, and sporting a half shirt, exposing her well-toned stomach. A'Man smiled like a man about to get lucky as he entered the house. But when he saw Joann's mother sitting on the sofa, his hopes of sex faded.

After Joann introduced A'Man to her mother, she invited him to her bedroom. As A'Man followed Joann upstairs, he looked back at Joann's mother, who gave him the evil eye.

Once they were in her bedroom, Joann wiped her hand across A'Man's crotch as she walked by him. Joann lay on her bed with her hands behind her head. She put her feet on the bed and pointed her knees upward. A'Man looked between Joann's legs and chuckled lightly, *no panties*.

"Damn, I feel kind of awkward with your mother being downstairs."

"I pay rent here."

"What's up with Rob?"

"Rob is my baby, but I don't want to talk about him."

"Do he show up here unannounced?"

"Yeah, why? You're scared he might come over tonight?"

"No. I just don't want nobody walking in on me."

"He's not coming over here...come here, unless you want to talk about Rob."

A'Man was uncomfortable. He thought better of sticking around and the possibility of confronting a jealous man. The whole scene—mom downstairs and Rob liable to walk in at any minute—was a little risky for A'Man's taste. But staring at Joann's exposed runner's legs was a temptation too much for A'Man to resist.

A'Man moved to the bed and lay next to Joann. He rubbed between her legs in that warm place and kissed her stomach. While he circled her belly button with his tongue, Joann moaned. Just then, a knock on the door interrupted the foreplay. A'Man's heart bolted. He jumped off the bed, uncertain of what to do. Surprisingly, Joann seemed calm. She only cursed out of frustration as she climbed off the bed and opened the door.

"Mom, you know I have company?"

In a whispered voice, mom said, "Rob's right outside parking his car, you need to get your shit together. I'm tired of this. You're lucky I just happened to look out the door and saw him drive up."

After Joann's mother walked to her bedroom, Joann shook her head at A'Man, who had overheard the conversation.

"You have to go," Joann said.

"Shit! What you want me to do, just walk by him?"

"Do you think I'm stupid? Come on?"

A'Man followed Joann to the kitchen.

"When me and Rob go upstairs, leave and I'll call you tomorrow, alright."

"Yeah."

Joann kissed A'Man, then she walked into the living room and sat down. A minute later, Rob knocked on the door. When A'Man was sure that Rob and Joann were in her bedroom, he left.

A'Man sat in his car, closed his eyes, and smacked his head against the headrest a couple of times out of frustration. For the jilted playboy, nothing was more exasperating than being a kiss away from making love to a beautiful woman, only to have to sneak out of her house due to the unexpected arrival of the husband or lover.

A'Man glanced at his watch, it was 11:30 p.m. With his sexual appetite in need of fulfillment, A'Man drove to Dawn's apartment.

Dawn was awakened by the sound of her doorbell. As the ringing continued, she lay in bed debating whether to answer the door or hope her ex-boyfriend would get the message and leave. Dawn had no doubt that it was A'Man responding to the message she left on his voicemail.

When it seemed that A'Man wasn't going to leave, Dawn made up her mind that tonight would be the night she dissolved any association with him.

Dawn climbed out of bed naked. She was accustomed to sleeping in the nude. Her first intent was to slip on a pair or sweatpants and a t-shirt, but the intense ringing of the doorbell was so annoying, she just put on a bathrobe and hurried to the door.

When A'Man entered the apartment, he kissed Dawn on the cheek and took a seat on the sofa. Lost on him was Dawn's displeasure with the kiss. Dawn stood across from A'Man with her arms folded across her chest. In spite of the fact that she was garbed in her bathrobe, she was all business. A'Man took notice, but he believed her stony demeanor was a façade to hide her desire to be all over him.

"You can't come here at anytime of the night."

"I got your message."

A'Man grinned at Dawn. She lowered her head, ready to succumb to embarrassment. But she fought the shame and glared at A'Man until he stopped grinning.

"That message was a mistake."

"That was a pretty long speech to be a mistake...I can stick it anywhere, huh?"

Dawn sucked her teeth and rolled her eyes at A'Man before walking off. A'Man stood and headed over to Dawn, standing inches away from her.

"Dawn, I'm sorry about everything that happened with Tracy. Tracy was a mistake. I got caught up. She came on to me, I was smoking weed. But tonight I'm where I want to be. Tracy and I are moving in two different directions."

"Is she still at your house?"

"Only because she don't have anywhere to stay. Leaving you was a mistake, the biggest I ever made. I got caught up in wanting to help Tracy get her daughter back."

While A'Man continued to confess his sins, mistakes, and dying desire to get back with Dawn, her resistance was weakening. A'Man saw the firmness that was once on her face disappear. He pulled Dawn close and kissed her with the passion of a man in love. Dawn closed her eyes and kissed him back.

In the midst of kissing, Dawn envisioned Tracy crawling from underneath A'Man's bed. Dawn broke away from A'Man and shook her head "no." She sat on the sofa and cupped her face in her hands.

"No. I won't do this. A'Man, please leave. I'm not falling for your lies. Go be with Tracy, and I truly wish y'all well."

"Come here, girl."

"No."

A'Man walked in front of Dawn and just stared down at her.

"Leave me alone, I'm moving on."

"You know you want me."

Dawn stood up, facing A'Man.

"I'm good, I don't want a man who doesn't respect me nor himself. I will never be the other woman again."

"What are you talking about?"

A'Man reached for Dawn's bathrobe and opened it from the top, just enough to see her breast. She smacked his hand, causing him to withdraw it.

"Stop it."

"You know you want me."

As A'Man playfully attempted to open Dawn's bathrobe, she smacked his hand and held the bathrobe closed with both hands. A'Man pried her hands free at the wrist and held her hands up to her face while he kissed her neck. Dawn frowned and squinted her nose as she took a whiff of Joann's scent that was still fresh on his fingers.

"Ill! Your fingers stink like pussy. You're still fucking with those nasty bitches! You're disgusting!"

A'Man squeezed Dawn's wrist.

"Ouch, you're hurting me!"

"You called me over here for this."

A'Man wrestled Dawn to the carpet floor faced down. Before she could stand, he was upon her, pinning her down with the weight of his body and anger.

"Get off me!"

"You said I can get rough!"

"Get the hell off of me!"

"I can stick it anywhere right?"

As Dawn struggled unsuccessfully, A'Man choked her and fulfilled his desires, invading her forbidden zone and her conscious while she begged for him to stop!

It got to the point where Dawn gave up her struggle and allowed him free reign over her body. Every second of the ordeal she cursed, and inside she prayed that he would soon be done with his assault of her.

Although the assault lasted no more than five minutes, to Dawn, it seemed to go on for hours. Afterwards, A'Man stood slowly, looking down at Dawn and gauging her reaction.

Naturally, Dawn was angry and humiliated. Out of the corner of her eye she saw A'Man watching her, but she avoided direct eye contact with him.

"Dawn?"

Dawn didn't answer. She picked herself up from off the floor, crossed the room, and picked up the telephone.

"You're going to prison for a long time!"

"Stop playing, girl."

Dawn punched the 9 with the intent of dialing 911, but before she could complete the call, A'Man snatched the phone away and hung it up.

"Girl, what do you think you're doing?"

Although A'Man believed Dawn was bluffing about calling the police, he wasn't taking any chances.

"You raped me!"

For some oddball reason, A'Man didn't regard his actions as rape. He looked into Dawn's serious eyes, and for the first time, he had no doubts that she meant business. A'Man started thinking fast to save his hide from any potential prosecution.

"Now wait a minute, Dawn, we're having a misunderstanding of events. You called me over here."

"No, I didn't!"

"I may have gotten a little rough-handed, but I didn't rape you...if you didn't want to do nothing, why did you answer the door naked?"

"Call it what you wish. Give me the phone!"

"Dawn, calm down. Think about what you're about to do. You wanted this as much as I did. I have you on my voicemail talking about I can stick it anywhere and I can get rough."

Dawn looked like a rug was pulled from under her. From her experience as a lawyer, she was well aware of the many rape cases where a savy defense attorney would flip the script in the courtroom, and suddenly the rape victim is defending herself, instead of the accused answering the charges against him. Dawn thought about the message she left on the voicemail and cursed silently. The voicemail would not only be detrimental to a criminal case, it would also be embarrassing to her career.

Dawn chuckled in disbelief at the turn of events. A'Man sat next to her. For a moment he didn't speak, nor did she.

"I'm sorry, Dawn. Things got out of hand."

Dawn didn't respond. She was starting to question her own actions. Knowing that it was A'Man ringing the bell at 11:30 p.m., why didn't she put on a pair of pants and a shirt. She wondered if subconsciously she wanted something to happen between them.

"Dawn, what are you thinking about?"

Again, Dawn didn't respond, and A'Man didn't push for a reply. They sat there silently trying to put their thoughts in perspective. As Dawn was deciding that there was nothing she could do legally to A'Man, her thoughts shifted to a violent alternative. She could lure him into the kitchen and stab him in the gut. But a part of her didn't want to harm him.

While Dawn struggled with her feelings, A'Man placed his arm around her. Dawn removed his arm and gave him the are-you-crazy glare.

"Dawn, I know you're probably thinking about should you get me locked up or shoot me or something. I admit that I was out of line."

"You were more than out of line!"

"I'm sorry. Dawn, I really thought this is what you wanted."

In spite of everything that had occurred that night, Dawn and A'Man talked into the night, and surprisingly, they both fell asleep on the sofa.

The following morning, Dawn awoke with her head on A'Man's chest. As he lay there snoring, she crept into the kitchen and grabbed a knife. As she stood there ready to get her revenge, she thought about going to prison and then placed the knife on the table, then she walked back to the living room.

"A'Man, get up."

A'Man awoke and looked at his watch. Although he was pissed for falling asleep on Dawn's sofa, he didn't show it.

"Dawn, I'm going home to shower, then I'll come back and we can finish talking."

"A'Man, don't come back. There's nothing here for you."

With that, Dawn walked into the bathroom and locked the door. A'Man hurried out of the apartment and stopped in his tracks when he saw Sam approaching. She saw him and dropped her head in disbelief.

"What are you doing here?" Sam asked.

A'Man winked at Sam.

"You think you really hot shit, don't you?"

A'Man started to ignore Sam and proceed on his way, but his egotistical nature got the best of him.

"Maybe next time your friends and I might have a threesome, or we could have a foursome."

Sam smacked A'Man and clenched her fist, ready for a fight. Although the smack had stung, A'Man took it in stride and strolled past Sam towards his car.

"A'Man, you're a pussy!"

Dawn had started running a hot bath when she heard the doorbell. She sighed with the belief that it was A'Man, since he had left only a few minutes ago and she wasn't expecting any company. This time, Dawn had no intentions on letting him in for part two of the episode from last night.

Dawn ignored the bell and continued preparing her bath. Moments later, her cell phone rang. She answered the call and was surprised when Sam told her to answer the door.

Sam was indignant when she walked into Dawn's apartment. As soon as Dawn shut the door, Sam was in her face.

"Have you and Tracy gone mad? You two bitches are crazy!"

"You saw A'Man?"

"How could you do it, Dawn?"

"Before you start judging and assuming, hear me out."

"What's there to hear? You had him first, so fuck Tracy?"

"You don't know what you're talking about."

"I have one question. Did you and A'Man have intercourse?'

Dawn turned away from Sam and walked across the room. She stood with her back to Sam. Sam threw her hands up in the air, believing she had gotten her answer based on Dawn's body's language.

"How could you sleep with him after what he did to you? Forget that it was Tracy, it could've been any woman. Are you that desperate?"

"You don't know what the fuck you're talking about!"

"You fucked him, Dawn!"

"No, I didn't! He raped me!"

The admission stunned Sam. She watched the tears spill down Dawn's cheeks and knew the allegation wasn't a joke or excuse for sleeping with A'Man.

"Oh my God. Did you call the police?"

"No."

"Well, call them."

"No, forget about it."

"What? Forget nothing, you have to report this!"

"I don't want to talk about it."

Dawn sat on the sofa. Sam joined her.

"He threatened you, didn't he?"

Sam was shocked as Dawn slowly related how, in a moment of weakness, she left the despicable message on A'Man's voicemail. After he raped her and she threatened to call the police, A'Man told her that he would use the voicemail message against her in court. Even though Sam understood Dawn's predicament, she disagreed with not reporting the assault.

"I'm going to tell Andrew," Sam said.

"No! Don't say nothing to him. I don't want him to get in trouble behind me. You know his temper. I shouldn't have left the message or let him in here. I'm just going to move on. Let Tracy deal with him. Sooner or later she'll see A'Man for who he is. I actually feel sorry for her. I need to take a bath, I'll call you later."

"I'll stay over."

"No, I'm good."

"You're sure?"

"Yes. And promise me you won't mention this to Andrew."

"I promise."

CHARLIE BASSETT JR.

After giving Dawn a tight hug, Sam hurried out of the apartment.

Meanwhile, A'Man walked up to his front door and paused. When he glanced at his watch, he caught a glimpse of his wrinkled clothes. He looked up at the bright sky and sighed. He started to make up an excuse about his whereabouts but nixed the idea. As he inserted his key and opened the door sliently, he hoped that Tracy was asleep.

A'Man quietly entered the house and saw Tracy on the sofa asleep with a blanket over her. A'Man tiptoed towards the stairs, but before he got there, Tracy sat up. A'Man turned around towards her, ready for an argument. But Tracy had made up her mind earlier that she wasn't going to fly off the handle with accusations and suspicious questions.

"Are you okay? I was worried about you."

"Yeah, I'm alright. I saw you sleeping and didn't want to wake you up."

"Did you take care of your business?"

"Yeah."

A'Man waited for another question, but it didn't come. Tracy lay back down and pulled the blanket over her head. A'Man smiled, believing that he had set her straight about questioning him. As he mounted the stairs, Tracy sat up again. A'Man thought, *here comes the drama.*

"A'Man, do you want me to cook you something to eat?"

"No, I'm good. I'm just going to jump in the shower and get some sleep."

A'Man proceeded upstairs and prepared for a shower, while Tracy stood from the sofa with the blanket draped over her shoulders and headed for the stairs. Halfway to the stairs, she was startled with fear by a heavy banging on the front door.

Her first thought was that it was the police for some illegal business A'Man had engaged in, but when she looked out the window and saw that it was Sam, she was confusingly surprised. She quickly opened the door.

250

"Where is he?"

"Sam, what's going on?"

"Your boyfriend raped Dawn?"

Tracy went to respond, but shock had stolen her voice. She looked at Sam questionably, hoping against all odds that Sam was somehow kidding. But Sam's stern face and hate-filled eyes left little room for one to believe otherwise.

"A'Man wouldn't rape Dawn."

"I knew you would defend him! I knew it! You're so fucked up over him you can't see your own hand if you held it in front of your face."

"Why are you starting trouble?"

"A'Man is the trouble. Call Dawn if you don't believe me. Twenty minutes ago I saw him leave her house. He was talking about a foursome with you, me, and Dawn!"

Tracy was furious.

"At first I thought she had consensual sex with him, until she told me the story…"

"What story was that?" asked A'Man.

A'Man strutted down the stairs wearing a pair of jeans and shirtless. Sam headed towards him, but Tracy rushed in front of Sam and held her from physically attacking A'Man, while he stopped at a safe distance in the middle of the stairs.

"You raped her!"

"Raped who?"

"Don't play dumb. You raped Dawn!"

A'Man chuckled and said, "Really? Why would I rape Dawn? If I was going to rape someone, would it be Dawn?"

That made sense to Tracy. She looked at Sam, hoping that Sam saw the logic in A'Man's statement. But Sam wasn't in love with A'Man and eager to believe his lies as was Tracy.

"A'Man, did I just see you leave Dawn's house about a half-hour ago?"

"That's a lie," said Tracy.

"You saw me," A'Man nonchalantly replied.

Tracy was struck stupid, she turned slowly and glared at A'Man in disbelief. Sam looked vindicated. Having A'Man admit the truth seemed to settle Sam down a bit, but she still had a lot of fire in her eyes.

"And this is the motherfucker you're in love with," said Sam.

A'Man strolled past the two women and entered the kitchen with the girls in pursuit. He opened the refrigerator, looking inside.

"A'Man, what's going on?" Tracy asked.

"You believe I raped Dawn?"

"I just want to get to the bottom of things."

"He raped her," Sam interjected.

"If I raped her, why didn't she call the cops? Why aren't the cops here and you are?"

"You know why she didn't call the police!"

"Why was you at Dawn's house in the first place?" Tracy said.

"Tracy, I'm going to tell you this because I love you. If I didn't care about you, I wouldn't waste my time saying that I didn't rape Dawn, and it's obvious why Sam is saying this. Furthermore, I resent you for accusing me of this nonsense."

"I didn't accuse you of anything," Tracy said.

"I did!" Sam said.

"After I took care of my business, I went to Dawn's house about forty-five minutes ago to ask her to make up with you and she came on to me. I rejected her and now she's screaming rape. I don't have to rape Dawn. I can fuck her anytime I want, but I don't want to be with her, I'm with you."

"Liar! You raped her, and because of that message, she won't go to the police."

Sam charged A'Man. They got into a shouting and wrestling match until Tracy finally separated them.

"Get the fuck out of my house!" A'Man screamed.

"Tracy, he's a fucking liar!"

"I didn't rape Dawn! Get out! You're mad because you want me!" A'Man retorted.

"Come one, Tracy, let's go!" said Sam.

"Sam, please leave," said Tracy.

"Tracy, can't you see he's no good?"

"Sam, just leave. I'll call you later."

With her heart breaking, Sam stared sadly at her friend. Tracy looked pitiful as she avoided eye contact with Sam. In a last effort to taunt Sam, A'Man pulled Tracy in front of him with her back to his chest and kissed her on the cheek.

"Oh, Tracy, may God help you," Sam said.

After Sam left the house, A'Man and Tracy didn't speak on the matter. He poured a glass of water, then he went upstairs to bed and slept like a newborn baby. Tracy sat at the kitchen table, feeling trapped in her own emotional triangle of pain, confusion, and uncertainty.

CHAPTER
21

A week had passed since Sam had informed Tracy that A'Man had raped Dawn, yet Tracy and A'Man, for whatever reason, refused to discuss the allegation. As far as their home life was concerned, the relationship was touch-and-go. Since the confrontation, Tracy and A'Man only slept together once, and the sex was mediocre to say the least. Tracy was slowly becoming a prisoner in her own mind, body, and unhealthy relationship.

Tracy finished her shower, entered the bedroom, and dressed in a pair of jeans and a pullover-hooded sweatshirt while A'Man lay in bed watching her. He, too, felt that the relationship was suffering, but it was not A'Man's nature to be affectionate when a woman really needed him to be, unless it was for his own benefit.

"Can you give me a ride to pick up Tammy?'

"I'm tired. I'll take you in an hour?"

"That's alright, I'll take the bus."

Tracy had hoped that A'Man would climb out of bed, but being the selfish prick that he was, A'Man turned on his side and went back to sleep.

Three hours later, Tracy and Tammy were leaving a fast-food restaurant while Dawn was entering. When the two women saw each other, they stopped in their tracks. Both women were waiting for the other to say something. However, before a word would be spoken, Tammy jumped into Dawn's arms. Tracy looked uncomfortable, but she didn't intervene.

"Hi, Aunt Dawn."

"Hey, Tammy."

"We just ate, are we going to your house?"

"No. I have to eat my lunch and then I'm going shopping."

"Oh...I miss going to your house."

"I miss you, too, Tammy."

"My mother and her boyfriend took me to Chuck E. Cheese."

"Did you have fun?"

"Yes. But I don't like my mommy new boyfriend. Do you?"

Both Tracy and Dawn were stunned by Tammy's admission. Although Dawn wanted to say I hate the motherfucker, she reserved her feelings. Tracy tried but failed to hide her anger.

"Tammy, come here," Tracy commanded.

Tammy saw the look on her mother's face and lowered her head. At that moment, with saddened eyes, Dawn gave Tracy a challenging look. At that instant, Tracy saw Dawn no longer as an enemy or rival, but as the friend she once had. Tracy desperately wanted to apologize for the pain in Dawn's eyes. Tracy also wanted to question Dawn about the rape. But pride intervened on both issues.

Dawn lowered Tammy to the floor and kissed her on the cheek.

"You take care, Tammy," Dawn said.

With a stern face, Dawn walked away without another word or look in Tracy's direction.

• • •

Sam stopped her car at the busy intersection. While she waited for the light to change, her daughter that was sitting in the back seat asked her a question. As Sam turned around towards the child, she caught a glimpse of A'Man's car driving by at a slow speed.

Sam turned forward and focused on the departing car. She watched long enough to see that there was a woman in the passenger's seat, and the woman wasn't Tracy. Although Sam managed to catch only a side profile of the woman, she thought the woman looked a lot like Tracy's cousin Joann.

Prodded by her curiosity, Sam looked for a clearance in the traffic and made the illegal turn on the red light. Fortunately for her, she could still see A'Man's car up ahead in the distance. But unfortunately, she would never reach him, no thanks to the cop that pulled her over for running the red light.

As Sam was waiting for the police officer to write out her ticket, she wondered how she was going to break the news to Tracy that A'Man was probably fooling around with Joann.

...

When Tracy took Tammy home to Steve's house, Tracy wasn't there two minutes before she was floored with the news that Steve was marrying his girlfriend and moving out of the city, and, of course, they were taking Tammy with them.

Faced with the heart-wrenching prospect of being further separated from her child, there was little Tracy could do but argue vehemently with Steve against taking Tammy away from her. But Tracy's argument was fruitless since Steve had full custody of Tammy.

Exhausted from arguing, Tracy kissed Tammy on her cheek, and then she stormed out of the house with tears in her eyes. As Tracy stood waiting for the bus, a cool rain began to fall. Tracy was so distraught that she didn't bother to pull her hood over her head.

While Tracy stood in the rain—without bothering to seek shelter or get an umbrella—she thought about Dawn and the look Dawn had given her earlier. In Tracy's gut, she was ninety percent sure that A'Man had not been truthful about the incident with Dawn, but Tracy couldn't bring herself to admit it. Suddenly, she felt the need to confront Dawn, once and for all, to find out what really happened.

A half-hour later, Tracy got off the bus at the corner of Dawn's apartment complex. As she walked towards the building, she almost chickened out and turned around.

...

Sam dropped her children off at the house with Andrew and was back out the door. She couldn't shake her gut feeling that the woman in A'Man's car was Joann, but she wanted to be certain. Before Sam started her car, she called Tracy and was surprised when Tracy said that she was outside of Dawn's apartment.

"Tracy, wait for me. I'll be by there in a little bit, but I have to make a stop first."

Ten minutes later, Sam drove slowly down Joann's block, and sure enough, her suspicions were confirmed when she pulled up next to A'Man's car, which was parked two cars down from Joann's house.

"Y'all dirty motherfuckers."

...

Meanwhile, Tracy rang Dawn's doorbell and waited with butterflies flying out of control in her stomach. After a couple more rings and no answer, Tracy was about to leave, when Dawn opened the door.

"What do you want?" asked Dawn.

"Hi," Tracy said hesitantly, "Dawn, I know you probably hate me. But I'm...this whole situation is messed up."

"Messed up! It's more than messed up. Things are fucked up."

"Just hear me out. I didn't pursue A'Man."

Dawn scoffed.

Tracy ignored the sarcasm and continued, "I just want to know...Sam told me that A'Man raped you. I just want to know if it was true. I don't want to get into an argument."

"Let me tell you something, yes, your fucking boyfriend raped me."

Tracy felt weak at the knees and her throat went dry.

"You know what, I'm going to tell you everything," Dawn said.

"Can I step in the hall?"

Dawn looked at Tracy for a moment, then she stepped to the side to allow Tracy to enter.

"A'Man told me that he didn't want to be with you and that you were a mistake. But I wasn't stupid enough to feed into his lies. He said you wasn't shit."

As Dawn's verbal assault began to get underneath Tracy's skin, Tracy felt hurt, but she remained silent and took her medicine.

"A'Man ain't shit. He's a bum," Dawn said.

Believing that Tracy knew about the message left on A'Man's voicemail, Dawn wanted to explain herself to clarify the matter.

"I know A'Man probably told you that he only came over to the apartment that night because of the message I left on his voicemail. Yes, I said I wanted to be with him and let him do whatever he wanted to me, but..."

Oh, he can do whatever he wants to you, Tracy thought.

Until that point, Tracy was feeling guilty and was slowly coming to her senses about A'Man, but after hearing about the message, Tracy was now looking at Dawn suspiciously like it was Dawn, and not A'Man, who was the liar. Tracy thought about A'Man's statement that he didn't have to rape Dawn. Tracy looked Dawn up and down and agreed with A'Man's statement.

"Yes, A'Man is rotten to the core. And you're stupid to still be with him."

As Dawn continued to ridicule both A'Man and Tracy, she couldn't see that Tracy was getting worked up. Suddenly, Tracy lunged forward without warning and grabbed Dawn by the hair. The women began tussling, with Dawn getting the worst of it. Sam arrived just in time. She opened the door, rushed inside, and broke up the fight.

"Stop it!" Sam yelled.

"Tracy, you lost you damn mind! I should press charges and have you sent back to jail!" Dawn screamed.

Tracy didn't respond. She walked out of the complex into the rain. Again, she didn't bother to put on her hoodie.

"Why we're y'all fighting?"

"Ask that crazy bitch, she attacked me! Sam, get her away from here before I call the police, I'm not joking!"

"Dawn, I'll talk to you later."

Sam walked outside and stepped in front of Tracy, who had a distant look in her eyes.

"Tracy, is A'Man worth all this?"

"Can you take me home?"

As Sam drove with Tracy in the passenger's seat, the two women didn't say a word to each other. Sam thought that she could add Tracy to the long list of forlorn women who were so in love with a good-for-nothing man that they couldn't see the forest for the trees.

Sam reckoned that it was time for some tough love for Tracy, and she hoped the lesson was still at Joann's house. When Sam made the turn onto Joann's block, Tracy looked at her questionably.

"What are you doing?"

Sam didn't respond. She drove down the block, stopping beside A'Man's car. Tracy looked at Sam, then she looked to A'Man's car.

"Park, Sam."

Tracy exited the car. Her first impulse was to knock on Joann's door and cause a ruckus. But she controlled her anger and walked across the street from Joann's and stared at the house as she waited.

Sam started to join Tracy but decided to watch from the dryness of the car and let the situation play out whichever way it would.

For ten minutes, Tracy stood like a statue in the rain. Her emotions were whirled. The fire in her head was torching her entire insides. Finally, the door opened, revealing the bad news as A'Man kissed Joann goodbye.

"A'Man!" Tracy yelled.

Sam hopped out of the car. A'Man and Joann disengaged at the roar of Tracy's voice. They both looked stunned as they saw Tracy with the rain pattering on her face and head.

Tracy clenched her fist and headed towards the couple, but she stopped in the middle of the street. Tracy's rapid breathing became measured. Suddenly, she lost her aggression and her will to fight. It was like she lost the spirit inside of her. Her tears of anger turned to tears of defeat. In a surprise to everyone, Tracy turned away from the cheaters and ran down the block at top speed.

"Tracy!" Sam yelled.

Sam gave chase, but Tracy quickly lost her.

When Sam jogged back to Joann's block, A'Man was getting into his car. Sam held open his car door, preventing him from closing it.

"You're not going to be satisfied until somebody do something to you."

Sam hopped in her own car and circled the neighborhood, searching for Tracy. When she couldn't locate her friend, Sam drove to A'Man's. With Tracy a no-show, Sam made a stop at Mr. Charlie's, but he hadn't heard from Tracy since they had broken up.

Sam went home and called Tracy several times, only to get Tracy's voicemail.

...

While Dawn stared into the mirror at the scratches on her face from Tracy's fingernails, her cell phone rang.

FRIENDS

"Hello! Sam, I'm busy right now. What?"

As Sam related what happened to Tracy, Dawn listened with no signs of emotions or concern.

"She could run into a brick wall for all I care," said Dawn, then she hung up.

CHAPTER
22

Sam rushed into Temple Hospital, not knowing what to expect. She prayed that Tracy's condition wasn't serious. For three days Sam had called every hospital in the city, the police stations, and even the morgue. Finally, she discovered that Tracy was in the psychiatric unit in Temple Hospital.

When Sam conversed with the resident psychologist, all she would do is hold her hand over her mouth and listen. The doctor said that Tracy was brought in by the police two days earlier, at which time Tracy was incoherent and sporting a fresh black eye.

The police report stated that when the officers picked Tracy up, she had been walking down the street mumbling, and she was wearing a soiled hooded sweatshirt, her panties, and socks. When Tracy was asked where were her pants, the officers reported that she mumbled something about her cousin had worn them before. And she couldn't remember who had hit her in the eye.

Once at the hospital, Tracy was given a physical examination. There was no sign of sexual assault; however, she had suffered from a nervous breakdown.

When Sam entered the room and saw how pitiful Tracy looked, Sam's eyes welled with tears.

...

Dawn was in her office when the receptionist informed her that there was a woman in the outer office who didn't have an appointment but urgently needed to see her.

"What's her name?"

"Monica. She didn't give a last name."

"Who the hell is Monica?"

When Dawn walked into the outer office, Monica smiled, then she embraced Dawn as if they were old friends.

"Hey, Dawn."

Dawn stepped back, looking inquisitively at Monica. Dawn was trying to place her, but she couldn't.

"I'm Monica...Tracy's old cellie."

Obviously Tracy didn't tell you what happened between us, Dawn thought.

"I got out yesterday. I stopped by the apartment but no one was there, so I came here. Where's Tracy, she not working today?"

"Tracy doesn't work here nor does she live with me."

"What?"

Dawn wrote down a number on a piece of paper and handed it to Monica.

"If Tracy told you about me, I'm sure she mentioned Sam."

"Yeah."

"This is Sam's number, give her a call, she'll give you the information on Tracy."

"What's up with Tracy?"

"Give Sam a call. I have to get back to work."

Monica looked at Dawn for a moment, searching for more questions.

"Tracy's in the hospital, call Sam. Now, I must get back to work."

From the irritation in Dawn's voice, it didn't take long for Monica to understand that there had been some rift between Tracy and Dawn, so Monica thanked Dawn for the number, then she rushed out the door.

• • •

Tracy smiled when she saw Sam.

"Hi, Sam."

After the women embraced, Sam stepped back and gave Tracy a look over.

"Tracy, what happened?"

"They say I have to take some medicine."

"What happened? Who hit you?"

"The bad people."

"What?"

Sam squinted with her mouth agape.

"I'm joking. But I honestly don't remember."

"Do you remember running away from me?"

"No."

Tracy sat down, looking upset for her lack of memory. Sam pulled a chair in front of Tracy. The women talked for a few minutes and Tracy seemed to be well, in spite of her lack of memory. But when Sam mentioned A'Man's name, Tracy snapped. She began screaming that Steve was stealing Tammy from her, and that everyone was out to get her. Tracy became so hysterical that Sam had to call for staff. When the doctor saw Tracy's condition, he asked Sam to leave while they assisted Tracy. Sam mouthed the words "I love you" to Tracy, and then she left.

While Sam stood outside the room drying her tears and pulling herself together, her cell phone rang. Sam was shocked that it was Monica. Since Tracy had spoke often about she and Monica's closeness, Sam agreed to meet Monica in a nearby restaurant.

...

Dawn sat at her desk deep in thought about Tracy's situation. On one hand, Dawn still held resentment toward Tracy for taking A'Man. On the other hand, after hearing that Tracy mentally slipped, Dawn felt sorry for her.

Dawn decided that she was going to visit Tracy. Dawn grabbed her pocketbook and headed for the door, then she stopped. Something inside of her said don't go. So Dawn sat back down and tried to get Tracy off of her mind, but she was unsuccessful.

• • •

Monica sat in total shock as Sam related everything about the situation between Dawn, Tracy, Joann, and A'Man. Sam even told Monica about the one-night stand that she had with the playboy.

It brought tears to Monica's eyes as she heard about Tracy's condition.

After Monica extracted all the information she needed regarding A'Man's residence and hangouts, she stood up from the table.

"Sam, thanks for meeting me?"

"Why did you want to know so much about A'Man?"

"From what he did to y'all, I just want to know who he was just in case I run into him and he come on to me. There's an old saying that once you know fire burns, you won't stick your hand in it."

"I feel you."

In spite of Sam's response, she felt it was more to Monica's inquiry.

Monica and Sam promised to stay in touch, and then they departed.

• • •

Later that evening, Dawn was sitting with Sam and Andrew in their living room chatting. They went from one trivial conversation to the next. During the discussions, Dawn and Sam exchanged cryptic looks periodically. Andrew finally got the hint that the women wanted their privacy, so he went upstairs.

"When I went to see Tracy, she had a black eye," Sam said.

"She shouldn't be in the streets starting trouble."

"How do you know she started something?"

Dawn didn't respond.

"Tracy can't even remember what happened to her. We were having a conversation, and out of nowhere, she snaps. She was screaming about everyone is against her and Steve's taking Tammy away from her. It was crazy."

"Because the bitch is crazy."

"Tracy isn't crazy. She just got overwhelmed and had a breakdown."

"She shouldn't be a weak bitch and her head would be on straight."

"Dawn, you don't care at all?'

"No. She fucked me over. I don't give a fuck what happens to her. I told her that what she did to me with A'Man, somebody was going to do it to her. It's not my fault that it was Joann?"

"Monica seems cool and she cares about Tracy."

"Yeah...God only knows what they were doing in that cell when the lights were out."

"Stop that. You know Tracy isn't gay."

"I'm just saying, this chick shows up out of nowhere..."

"She just got out...she asked a lot of questions about A'Man."

"Maybe she wants to fuck him."

. . .

Clad in a tight dress, and looking sexy from head to toe, Monica stepped into the sports bar and stood in front of the door. Every man in the place turned to check her out. This was the reaction she expected and wanted. A moment later, Monica headed over to the bar while hungry eyes followed her.

Sam told Monica that this was the sports bar that A'Man was known to frequent.

As Monica nursed her drink, she scanned the bar. Whenever the door opened, she quickly looked in that direction. Although she had never saw A'Man in person, she was sure that she could recognize him by the description Sam gave.

As the minutes passed, several men tried to hit on Monica, but she politely rejected each of their advances. Monica thought first about Tracy and prayed that she would pull herself together.

Suddenly, the door opened. In walked a gentleman whom Monica believed fit A'Man's description. She gulped down her drink, then she crossed the room and intentionally bumped into the man.

"Excuse me," said Monica.

Then Monica and the man's eyes met. She could see that he was interested.

"It's okay, baby," the man said.

Not wanting to appear obvious, Monica gave the man a smile and walked away slowly. Monica could feel his eyes on her. A few seconds later, as Monica expected, the man approached her. Although Monica was disappointed when she learned the guy wasn't A'Man, she still took his phone number for future reference. A half-hour later, Monica called it a night and went home.

• • •

Tracy lay awake and told herself that she had to get her head together. She made up her mind that what she wasn't able to control, she would just have to let go and live to fight another day. That included Tammy.

• • •

Across town in A'Man's bed, Joann lay snuggled underneath his arms.

"How long do you think Tracy will have to stay in the crazy hospital?" asked Joann.

"I don't know."

"You're going to still move her shit out of here, right?"

"I told you, yes. I'm a man of my word. But I got to warn you that this dick can drive a woman crazy."

"I'm not my cousin."

Both A'Man and Joann laughed at Tracy's expense, then they fell asleep.

CHAPTER
23

With tears streaming down their cheeks, Monica and Tracy embraced tightly while professing how much they missed each other. For a moment, they disengaged to take a look at each other; then, they re-embraced. Finally, they sat down.

"Sam told me everything. Don't get angry, but how did you get with A'Man?"

Tracy stood quietly. She had asked herself that very question a hundred times without having an answer, but today, at that moment, she knew why.

"When I first hooked up with A'Man, I didn't like the person I was and I believed his lies and allowed myself to be defined by him. He has a clever tongue. The next thing you know, I'm trapped. I had no place to live."

Monica could see that Tracy was becoming troubled by the subject.

"Okay, that's history. I'm home now. What did I tell you while we were in jail, huh? I make things happen! The doctor said you're getting out of here in a couple of days. You're going to stay with me. After today, don't worry about A'Man, he's about to trip over a stick."

"What do you mean?"

"Don't worry about it...I want you to make things right with Dawn. But if she doesn't accept your apology, fuck her."

...

Dawn stood in the hospital parking lot, debating whether to go inside. While Dawn hesitated, Sam parked her car and walked over.

"I'm glad you came. What are you waiting for?"

"Sam, I don't know, she crossed me."

"You don't have to hug and kiss her, just stay a couple minutes, then leave."

On the other side of the parking lot, A'Man pulled in and parked. He had come to the hospital to see Tracy one last time before he dumped her. But when he saw Dawn and Sam, he changed his plans. He removed three large garbage bags filled with Tracy's clothes. He lugged them over to where Dawn and Sam were and dropped the bags at their feet.

"What is this?" Sam asked.

"Make sure your friend gets her shit."

"You rotten motherfucker!" said Sam.

Although Tracy wasn't Dawn's favorite person at the moment, Dawn was just as outraged as Sam.

Without warning, Sam swung wildly at A'Man, who covered well to avoid being hit by her. In the midst of the fight, Monica exited the hospital, but she stood at the entrance watching the altercation. Finally, Dawn restrained Sam. A'Man took the opportunity to walk briskly to his car. After A'Man drove off, Monica walked over.

"Was that A'Man?" Monica asked.

"That was the rotten motherfucker! I had to kick his ass!" Sam responded.

"Can you believe him? Bringing Tracy's clothes here," Dawn said.

"It's cool, Tracy's going to stay with me when she get out. Dawn, I need to speak with you about a private matter, I'll give you a call later. Can y'all help me take these bags to my car?"

When Monica drove away, Dawn said, "If she need for me to represent her in a case, she better have money."

CHAPTER
24

When Tracy was released from the hospital, she moved in with Monica. Actually, it was Monica's aunt's house. The aunt was happy to help Tracy after hearing about her situation.

It was 9:30 p.m. on a Friday night. Monica's aunt and Tracy were relaxing in the living room playing scrabble when Monica strutted down the stairs wearing a beautiful, ankle-length dress that wasn't too tight, but fitting enough to show off her curvaceous body.

"Where are you going?" Tracy asked.

"To see a man about a horse."

Monica winked her eye. Both Tracy and Monica's aunt burst into laughter.

A half-hour later, Monica stepped into the sports bar. She received the same gawking reaction that she had gotten a few days earlier.

On this particular night, there were a pair of eyes among the crowd that followed her to the bar. Monica smiled as she recognized that it was A'Man.

Not before long, A'Man approached Monica. She initially acted like she was disinterested. But as they conversed, Monica began to hang on to his every word. She giggled at his humor and occasionally patted his arm in a flirtatious manner. From Monica's behavior, A'Man knew he was making headway with the beautiful stranger.

"Let's get out of here?" A'Man said bluntly.

"You don't waste time, huh?"

"I'm saying we can go outside away from the noise and talk."

Monica glanced at her watch and frowned.

"It's getting late and I have an early morning...but we can get together tomorrow for lunch."

A'Man hesitated, then said, "Okay."

After they exchanged numbers, Monica went home and lay in bed. She smiled satisfactorily.

As for A'Man, he stopped by Joann's house and made love to her. All the while, he thought about Monica.

...

The following afternoon, A'Man met Monica for lunch in a quiet restaurant.

"What do you do, A'Man?"

"I'm laid off right now. In the meantime, I can make a woman feel like a queen."

"So you're a king, huh?"

"I'm just me, baby."

A'Man and Monica gazed at each other without speaking. She was attracted to him in a big way, but she held her feelings in check.

"What do you do for income?" Monica quizzed.

A'Man looked embarrassed. Before he could respond, Monica reached out and placed her hand on top of A'Man's and gazed back into his eyes.

"I like you, A'Man. I'm not trying to put you on the spot."

"What do you do, Monica?"

"I don't have a job. My family got money and they take care of me."

A'Man's eyes lit up. He thought he could have another money-chick like his ex-wife Mirrar on his hands. Hopefully, without the drama. After they finished lunch, Monica insisted on paying the tab. This boosted A'Man's already inflated ego. He chuckled inside, thinking that his charm had hooked another fish.

As the weeks followed, Monica continued to pay for lunch and dinners. Each time she met with A'Man, she brought a gift: clothing or jewelry. She even brought him a blender when she had visited his house and learned that he didn't have one.

A'Man had a speck of suspicion concerning Monica's generosity, but he reminded himself that she said that she came from money. On the occasions when A'Man asked to go over to Monica's house, she always had a legitimate excuse that he accepted.

Although Monica rejected A'Man's advances when he moved for sex, she did French kiss him, and she asked him to wait until she was ready because she was a virgin. A'Man's initial reaction was of shock, he didn't believe that there were any thirty- year- old virgins in the city, but after a long conversation on the subject, Monica made him a believer. The virgin lie also helped A'Man understand Monica's generosity; he assumed she was just inexperienced with men.

A'Man was living life with his head in the clouds. He knew he had finally found a winner, and he was seriously considering monogamy.

It was 3:30 a.m. Tuesday morning when Joann made an unannounced visit to A'Man's house. Since he had met Monica, he was seeing little of Joann, and although she was still in a relationship with Rob, she didn't appreciate being put on the back burner. In Joann's heart, she suspected that A'Man was seeing someone, and she also suspected that the other woman was inside.

Joann knocked on the door and waited. She had the audacity to wish that she had a key so she could catch A'Man in the act.

Groggily, A'Man opened the door and was surprised to see Joann.

"What's up, baby? What are you doing here?"

Joann didn't answer. She stepped inside, and then she darted up the stairs to A'Man's bedroom. To her surprise, the room was empty. A'Man entered and laughed.

"You thought somebody was here, didn't you?"

"Shut up. I know you're seeing somebody because you haven't been spending time with me."

"You know I love you girl and there's no one else."

"It better not be."

That morning, Joann made love to A'Man with the passion of a woman desperate to save her man.

A few hours later, A'Man awoke, showered, and dressed. He stood over Joann, watching her sleep. He had no regret for what he was about to do, but choosing Monica over Joann was a no-brainer.

Normally, A'Man would have juggled the women, but Monica was stepping up to the plate like a home-run hitter, and A'Man was determined not to screw things up.

"Joann, get up."

"Be quiet, I'm trying to sleep."

"Yo, get up. You have to go."

"What?"

"Yeah, I have a date and you gotta go."

"I thought you wasn't seeing no one?"

"See what happens when you think."

"Fuck you!"

As Joann dressed, she curse out A'Man and told him that's why she was still sleeping with Rob. A'Man showed no emotions, which angered Joann more. Finally, she smacked his face and left.

Later that afternoon, Monica arrived bearing gifts. A'Man kissed her hard on the mouth and tried to sweet-talk her to his bed. Although it was becoming difficult to resist his temptations, Monica managed.

Once A'Man came to grips that she wasn't going to his bed, he settled down and asked Monica what were the plans for the day.

Monica told A'Man that they were going to be doing a little shopping and have lunch, but first, she needed to drop her uncle's key off to him at his place.

When A'Man and Monica got into her car, Monica leaned over and kissed A'Man on the lips and told him that she was falling fast.

"I'm falling, too, baby."

"Tomorrow," Monica said.

"What?"

"I'll be ready tomorrow."

A'Man looked at Monica and knew she was talking about finally losing her virginity.

"A'Man, I have to use the bathroom."

A'Man handed his house key to Monica. She hopped out of the car, hurried into the house, then she returned moments later and smiling.

Twenty minutes later, Monica parked in front of a beautiful house on the outskirts of the city. A'Man noted that it was a luxurious neighborhood. Thus, validating Monica's story that her family had money.

"This is my Uncle James' house."

Once inside, Monica gave a short elderly man with suspicious eyes a hug.

"Uncle James, this is my boyfriend A'Man."

"A'Man?" James said.

"Yes, sir. That's my name."

Monica smiled like a proud girlfriend as the two men shook hands.

"Hi. How are you doing? This is a beautiful house," A'Man said.

"It is."

"Uncle James, here's your key."

James took the key. Then he turned to A'Man and looked him up and down.

"He looks and dresses a lot better than your last boyfriend."

A'Man smiled at the strokes of his ego.

"What's on the agenda for today?" James asked.

"We're going shopping and getting something to eat...come, A'Man," Monica said.

"It was nice to have met you," said A'Man.

"Shit!" Monica said.

Monica rifled through her pocketbook, then she made a face.

"What's wrong?" A'Man asked.

"I left my credit cards home. That's another trip on the other side of the city."

"We got time," A'Man said.

A'Man had never been to Monica's house and was anxious to see where she lived. Monica sighed and looked disappointedly at James.

"Don't look at me like that?" James said.

"You know I'll give you the money back. You know my mom got you if I don't have it when you want it."

"I don't have any cash. What about your friend?"

Monica shook her head "no" quickly at A'Man before James could see her.

"Uncle James, let me use one of your credit cards, please?"

James hesitated. Then he removed the platinum credit card from his wallet and handed it to Monica.

"Don't let her charge up the store."

"Alright," A'Man said.

Twenty minutes later in a leather and fur store, with A'Man standing by, Monica picked out three expensive coats and extended them to A'Man.

"Try on these, baby."

A'Man removed his own jacket and handed it to Monica. While A'Man tried on the jackets, Monica slipped something into A'Man's inside jacket pocket.

"Do you like them?" Monica asked.

"Yeah."

"Damn, I have to pee again. That herbal tea I drunk is running through me. Take the coats to the counter and sign for them."

"Sign?" A'Man inquired.

"Yeah, just write my uncle's name that's on the card. I have to use the bathroom. Wait for me here."

When A'Man signed for the coats, the pretty store clerk gave him a smile. It took major resistance for A'Man not to strike up a conversation with her.

Moments later, two men approached A'Man and told him that they were undercover police officers. They told A'Man that the credit card he had used was stolen.

A'Man tried to explain that the card belonged to his girlfriend's uncle and when she comes from the bathroom she would clear up everything.

While the officer patted A'Man down for weapons, the other officer reached into A'Man inside jacket pocket and removed the five identification cards with A'Man's picture and other individuals names.

"Wait! How did they get in my pocket! Y'all put them in there!"

Suddenly, the realization of what had happened sunk in. While the police handcuffed A'Man, his teary eyes searched the store for Monica, but she was nowhere to be seen.

A'Man paced the holding cell at the police station for hours. Finally, he was given a call. He phoned Dawn and begged her for help.

Three days later at the CFCF jail, a dispirited looking A'Man sat across from his attorney and ex-girlfriend Dawn.

"This shit is crazy. I met the bitch a couple of weeks ago and she's buying me all this shit. I thought she was just into me like that. Then I met her uncle and he gives her a credit card. They say the shit was stolen! Did you go to the address I told you?"

"Yeah, a young Caucasian couples lives there," Dawn said.

"What? No, that's James' house! They got me."

"Yeah...when they executed a search warrant at your house, they found stolen items and a bag full of oxycontin pills. I didn't know you were popping pills."

"I don't take drugs! The bitch must have planted the pills when she went to the bathroom!"

"A'Man, I don't think I can represent you. They have an open-and-shut case, and you and I are too close."

"I don't have money for a lawyer! I need you!"

Dawn paused, shaking her head "no."

"Dawn, I need you."

"A'Man, why would this girl set you up?"

"I don't know."

"A'Man, the best thing you can do is try to get a plea-bargain, you can't beat this case. They caught you red-handed."

A'Man looked like he wanted to die.

"I'm not going to admit to something I didn't do!"

CHAPTER
25

In the fairly empty courtroom, A'Man stood next to Dawn at the defense table, while the judge on the bench looked at him sternly.

"You have entered into the plea agreement with the State...I am sentencing you to five-to-ten years in the State Penitentiary."

"You did the right thing," Dawn whispered to A'Man.

While the sheriffs were putting the handcuffs on A'Man, the door to the courtroom opened. A'Man looked back and saw Tracy and Sam entering, followed by Monica.

"That's her!" A'Man yelled.

"Quiet!" the judge ordered.

A'Man ignored the judge and continued to yell that Monica was the girl who set him up. While the sheriffs were muscling a resisting A'Man out of the courtroom, he turned back just in time to see Monica and Dawn shake hands.

When A'Man got back to his jail cell, he vomited in the toilet. Then he curled up on his bunk and cried like a baby. His cellmate looked at him and laughed.

"You are a pussy," said the cellmate.

Across town in a restaurant, Tracy, Sam, Monica, and Dawn sat at a table with smiles all around.

"Now I have to think of something nice for Joann," said Monica.

"Leave it alone, it's time to move on," said Tracy.

"Are you sure?"

"Yes."

"We can use that energy to get Tammy back," Sam said.

The women nodded their heads in agreement.

"Monica, why did you keep me in the dark about what you were doing?" Tracy asked.

"I'm not trying to be smart, but when you're a part of something, things get fucked up."

Everybody laughed, save Tracy. Sam gave Tracy a friendly push, and then Tracy joined in the laughter.

"How did you do it?" Sam asked.

"Let me tell my story," said Dawn. "I had to take A'Man's case and convince him to take a deal. If he fought the case and got an investigator, who knows what could've happened. I kept telling him how tough the D.A. was with identity theft cases. He was shook."

"My part was easy, especially with men like A'Man who think that they are God's gift to women. First, I told him that my family had money that was the hook. And I backed it up by giving him gifts, which were purchased with stolen credit cards. I knew that A'Man might get suspicious of the gifts, so I told him that I was a virgin. He thought I didn't have experience with men and that I was a nut."

"If he paid attention to how you walked, he would've known that you wasn't a virgin," Tracy said.

"He saw how I walked, trust me. I took him to the Spaghetti Warehouse. They have a picture booth there. We took a couple of pictures, that's how I got his picture for the I.D.s. I know this guy who is a gardener. Everyday he feeds the dogs for this couple who was on vacation. I took A'Man to the house, he thought it was my uncle. The girl at the store knew what was going down and had the heads-up."

"How did you get all these people to go along with you?" Sam asked.

"We all used to be in a ring, we stole credit cards and shit. When I went to jail, it was for something I had nothing to do with. I kept my mouth closed and people owed me favors. After this twist with A'Man, I'm done with that life. I just wanted to help out my girl."

"Thanks," said Tracy.

"I keep my word." Monica said.

"I could've got disbarred for this," Dawn said.

"You didn't do nothing but tell a client to take a deal," Sam said.

"Thanks, Dawn I really appreciate this. I'm truly sorry about everything." Tracy said.

The women went silent for a moment.

"A'Man had it coming. No one should have any regrets," Sam said.

"A'Man got what he deserved...Oh, I still need a receptionist because my girl left," Dawn said.

"Can I get the job?" Monica asked.

Everyone gave her a look.

"I'm joking."

"Thank you," Tracy said in a choked-up voice.

"None of us are perfect...sometimes friendship needs to be tested," Dawn reminded.

THE END

FRIENDS

CHARLIE BASSETT JR.